Laboratory Manual For
Life Science
BSC1005L Third Edition

Geri Mayer • Michelle Cavallo

Contributing Authors:

Angela Bancalari-Schmidlapp, Emily King, Daniel Chauss, Chance Cowan, Ingrid Curril, Kristine Dunker, Judy Gocke, Jessica Klassen, Christopher Makowski, Larry Nissman, Lisa Rios, Mark Rochelo, Alya Singh

Florida Atlantic University, Boca Raton, FL

bluedoor
flexible & affordable learning solutions™

Chief Executive Officer: Jon K. Earl

President, College: Lucas Tomasso
President, Private Sector: Dawn Earl
Regional Manager: Greg Bartell

Senior Production Manager: Connie Dayton
Production Manager: Dan Woods
Digital Solutions Manager: Amber Wahl
Developmental & Production Coordinator: Rhiannon Nelson
Production Assistant: Ben Sweeney
Production Assistant: Erica Rieck
Production Manager: Stephanie Larson
Project Manager: Peggy Li

Consulting Editors: Bruce D. Wingerd, M.S.
                     Suzanne S. Frucht, Ph.D.
                     Anna M. Kats, M.S., Florida Atlantic University
                     Michelle F. Cavallo, M.S., Florida Atlantic University
                     John F. Wiginton, Ph.D., University of Mississippi
                     Stephanie R. Dillon, Ph.D., Florida State University

Cover Design: Erica Rieck

ISBN-13: 978-1-59984-813-6

Published by bluedoor, LLC
           10949 Bren Road East
           Minneapolis, MN 55343-9613
           800-979-1624
           www.bluedoorpublishing.com

Printed in the United States of America.
10 9 8

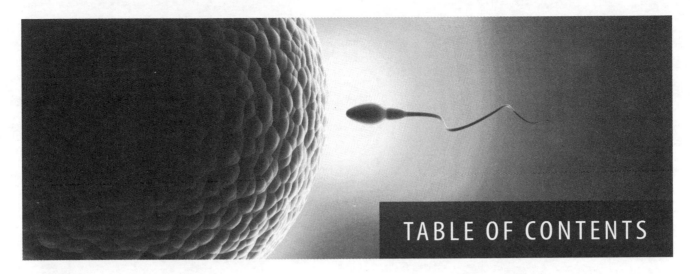

TABLE OF CONTENTS

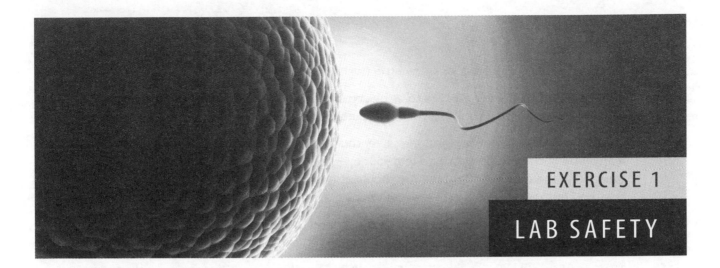

Welcome to Life Science lab. In lab you will get hands-on experience with what you've read about Biology. You will partake in various experiments that will allow you to test ideas, collect data, learn and apply biological concepts, and draw conclusions about what you have learned.

Objectives

The objectives of this lab are to learn about lab safety and to review general information that you will use in lab.

Before Coming To Lab:

Remember to read exercises before coming to lab. This will familiarize you with what will be done, save time, and help you finish lab successfully and in a timely manner.

While In Lab:

Before you start your experiment, your instructor will introduce the chapter and explain basic concepts, as well as the lab procedures; therefore, it is extremely important to listen to your instructor. Remember to stay focused as you work. You will be able to finish the exercise and learn from it if your mind is devoted to it. Remember to follow instructions and safety guidelines, which we will discuss a little later.

It is also important that you participate in lab wrap-up sessions in which concepts as well as differences in results, reasons behind results, and other pertinent information will be discussed.

General Safety:

- There is no eating, drinking, or smoking in the lab.

- Bookbags, books, purses, etc., are to be placed in the drawers or cabinets at the workstation. A clutter-free workbench should always be maintained.

- Locate the eyewash fountain and the safety shower (usually in the front of the classroom). If any type of chemical is splashed into your eyes, inform your instructor immediately, and proceed to the eyewash fountain. You should also inform your instructor if chemicals are splashed onto your skin. He/she will determine if a safety shower is necessary.

- If any type of glassware is broken, inform your instructor, and he/she will place it in the glass receptacle. Do not throw glass away in the regular trash receptacle.

- There is a first-aid kit in every lab; in it you will find bandages, antibiotic creams, etc. Any cuts should be immediately treated. For injuries requiring medical attention, contact the lab coordinator or student health services.

- When working with chemicals, make sure to wear proper eye protection. Eye goggles are provided in the lab.

- Exercise caution when using hotplates by never leaving them unattended and never touching the plate to test for warmth.

- Always use tongs (see last page) or a similar apparatus when handling hot glassware.

- Never use wet hands to plug in electrical devices.

- Place all biohazardous wastes in the proper receptacle. Do not place these wastes in regular trash containers. Biohazardous wastes are biologically contaminated waste, which include blood, saliva, urine, other bodily fluids, etc. Any waste from animal dissection should be placed in the biohazard bag. Paper towels and gloves used for dissection should also be placed in this receptacle.

- Anything reusable that has come in contact with biohazardous wastes should be washed thoroughly with a 10% bleach solution. Counters should also be wiped down with a disinfectant.

- Always wear gloves when dealing with biohazardous materials.

- Sharps (such as hypodermic needles, scalpel blades, and razor blades) have a special puncture resistant receptacle for disposal. If a sharp container is full, never force the item in; it can lead to puncturing yourself. Always exercise caution!

- After lab, hands should be thoroughly washed and countertops should always be wiped down.

- Unplug all equipment used in the lab, and return it to its proper place.

- Fire pulls and extinguishers are located in the hallways of the building. If you hear a fire alarm, proceed cautiously and calmly toward the exit and then outside. Be sure to familiarize yourself with these locations in case of an emergency.

Now let's learn how to perform a couple of tasks that will be asked of you in class.

Carrying A Microscope:

When removing a microscope from the cabinet, always use two hands, one holding it by its arm and the other supporting it under its base (**Figure 1**).

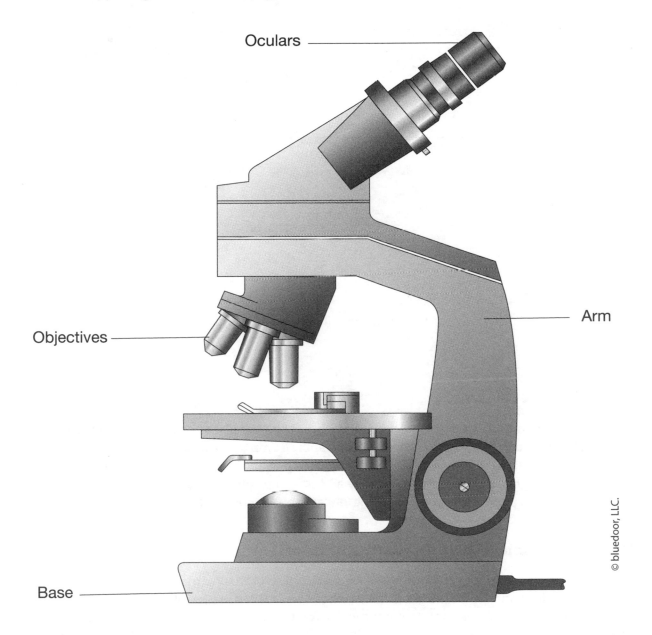

Oculars

Arm

Objectives

Base

© bluedoor, LLC.

Figure 1: Microscope.

Never carry a microscope by its objectives or oculars. Once the scope is plugged in, you may notice that it needs to be cleaned. This is simply done by using a piece of lens tissue and lightly but thoroughly wiping any fingerprints or dust from the microscope's lenses.

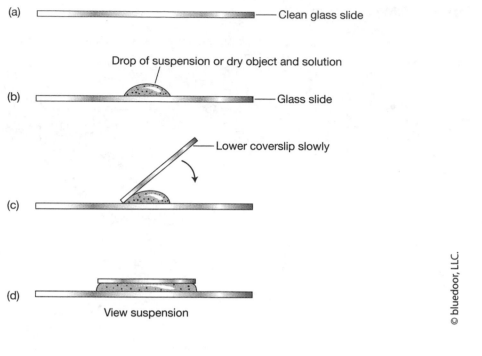

(a) ——— Clean glass slide

Drop of suspension or dry object and solution

(b) ——— Glass slide

——— Lower coverslip slowly

(c)

(d)

View suspension

© bluedoor, LLC.

Figure 2: Preparing a wet mount.

Preparing A Wet Mount:

To prepare a wet mount, simply take a clean microscope slide and place a small piece of your sample that is to be viewed in the middle of the slide. Next apply a drop of stain, saline solution, or water, depending on what you are viewing, and place a coverslip on top of it (**Figure 2**) Try to avoid air bubbles that can get trapped between the slide and coverslip. After you have finished observing, place the coverslip in the glass-only receptacle, discard your sample, and wash and dry your slide.

Weighing An Object Using An Electrical Balance:

In order to weigh an object, you must first place a watchglass or weighing paper on the scale and zero it. This is done so that the weight of the watchglass is factored in your lab weights. Next, place your object in the watchglass, and record the weight on the scale. There should not be anything leaning against the scale while you are weighing an object. Be sure to record the weight, including all decimal points.

On the following page there are figures of various utensils and glassware that you will be using in future labs, be sure to familiarize yourself with them.

Last, but not least, enjoy your lab!

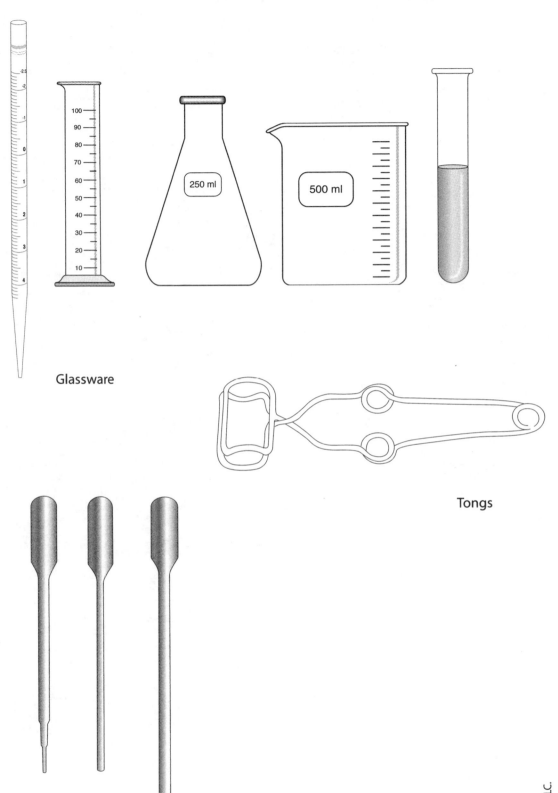

Glassware

Tongs

Pipette

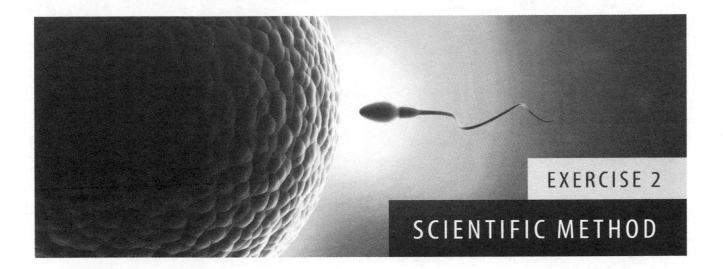

SCIENTIFIC METHOD

Objectives

The objectives of this exercise are to learn the steps of the scientific method and to use them to conduct an experiment.

INTRODUCTION

Science is about gaining knowledge. The word "science" comes from a Latin verb meaning "to know". The process known as the scientific method helps us to outline ideas and guides us through a series of steps to answer questions. However, imagination is just as important as the rigid steps of the scientific method. This method is also known as hypothetico-deductive reasoning. Let's break that down. *Hypothetico* refers to the word "hypothesis", a logical idea about the answer to a question. The deductive part refers to deductive reasoning: taking the general idea and coming up with specific results. For example: *If all living things are made of cells, and plants are living things...then plants must too be made of cells.*

There are eight basic steps to the scientific method. They are as follows:

1. Make an observation.

2. Ask a question.

3. Come up with a hypothesis.

4. Make a prediction based on your hypothesis.

5. Design an experiment to test your hypothesis.

6. Collect data.

7. Analyze your data.

8. Make conclusions about your data related to your hypothesis.

Remember Isaac Newton? Let's go through the steps to see how he used the scientific method to discover the law of gravity.

1. He observed an apple falling on his head.

2. He asked, "Why did that apple fall on my head? Furthermore, why do things fall toward the Earth instead of away from it?"

3. Newton hypothesized that there was some force acting on all objects that made them fall straight toward the Earth.

4. He made a prediction that this force could be identified and measured.

5. He designed an experiment to test this.

6. He then recorded data from his experiment.

7. He did a mathematical analysis to see if the differences were significant, or if they occurred by chance.

8. He made the conclusion that there is a force acting upon objects that make them move toward the Earth.

Another important thing to remember in designing an experiment is the addition of the **control**. The control is the treatment that stays the same. The **independent variable**, or thing you are manipulating during the experiment, is removed in the control.

As we discussed earlier in the chapter, the first step in any scientific investigation **is making an observation** of an interesting phenomenon. For example, Joe went to the store and purchased a plant when he moved into town. After three weeks, Joe's plant died. The death of Joe's plant is our observation. The next step in the scientific method is to **ask a question** about the observed phenomenon. In this case, the question would likely be, "Why did Joe's plant die?" Now you can generate one or more **hypothesis** (*i.e.*, make one or more educated guesses) that may potentially explain the death of Joe's plant. Below are several hypotheses about the death of Joe's plant:

1. Perhaps the plant got too much water.

2. Perhaps the plant got too little water.

3. Perhaps the plant got too much sunlight.

4. Perhaps the plant got too little sunlight.

5. Perhaps there were insufficient nutrients in the soil.

6. Perhaps the plant became root bound (*i.e.*, outgrew the pot).

These are just six possible explanations for the death of Joe's plant; there are many others. One point must be stressed: In science, we consider only one hypothesis at a time. In this case, we will consider hypothesis number 1: Perhaps the plant got too much water. Our next step is to make a **prediction** about our hypothesis. For example, we can predict that if Joe bought another plant and reduced the number of times that he watered it, then the plant would live longer.

Before designing an experiment for Joe, ask, "What is a good control for Joe's experiment?"

In the space below, **design an experiment** that Joe could do to test your hypothesis about the new plant.

Procedure

In this section of the course you will be developing a project based on the study of onions. To start off, you will have to develop your own scientific method for each experiment you will carry out. In this model, you will practice developing scientific methodology.

Think of an observation about your onion that you can test. [**Hint:** Size *vs.* Number of Roots; Size *vs.* Number of Onion Layers.]

Discuss with your group the different observations that can be made about onions. Two groups should work independently on each observation (your instructor will help you form the groups).

Now develop your hypothesis:

Make a prediction:

Design an experiment to determine if your prediction is correct:

Carry out the experiment and record your data in the space below:

Remember, a good experimental design will test only one hypothesis and must have a proper **control**. A control is a treatment or condition in which the independent variable (what you are varying during the experiment) is either removed, or set at a standard value.

What is a good control for your experiment?

At the end of your group work, make sure you have

1. made an observation,

2. asked a question,

3. come up with one or more hypotheses,

4. chosen one hypothesis, and made a prediction based on that hypothesis,

5. designed an experiment to test your hypothesis; your hypothesis never changes once you begin your experiment, regardless of your results.

6. collect data,

7. analyzed your data,

8. made conclusions about your data *in the context of the hypothesis being tested*, **AND** gave some reasonable explanations for your results. Conclusions do not make sense unless they are based on your hypothesis.

Now get back together with the whole class and compare your experiment with the other groups. Note the different types of observations, hypotheses, predictions, etc. Is there always a right or wrong answer?

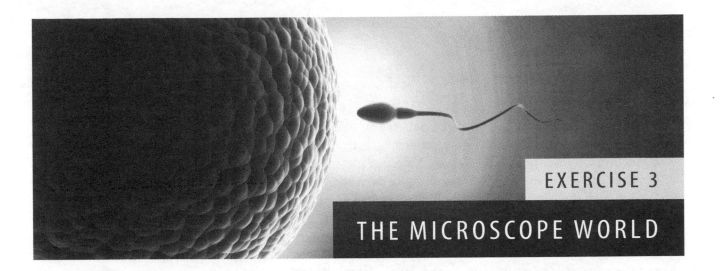

THE MICROSCOPE WORLD

Objectives

The objectives of this lab are to become familiar with the parts and operations of a compound and dissecting microscope, to understand orientation, field of view, brightness, depth of field, and to learn how to prepare a "wet mount".

INTRODUCTION

Before the microscope was invented, people thought there was nothing smaller than the smallest thing that could be viewed by the naked eye. Anthony Leeuwenhoek of Holland invented the first simple (single lens) microscope in the 1600s. Since its invention, the microscope has been a valuable tool in the development of scientific theory. A **compound light microscope** is composed of two elements, a primary magnification lens and a secondary lens system, similar to a telescope. Light is passed through an object and is then focused by the primary and secondary lens. The **dissecting microscope** or **stereoscope**, functions by bouncing light off of the specimen, instead of passing through it.

The function of any microscope is to enhance the **resolution** (clarity, sharpness) of an object. The microscope is used to **magnify** (apparent enhancement of an object) an object such that we can observe details not otherwise possible with the human eye. During this lab, you will be using both the **compound light microscope** and **dissecting microscope** (also known as the **stereoscope**) to observe various objects and slides.

Note: When carrying the microscopes, always use two hands. One hand should grip the arm; the other should support the base. This is expensive equipment, so be careful. If there is a problem with the microscope, inform your instructor.

Procedure 1

Dissecting Microscope (Stereoscope)

The dissecting microscope has a larger working distance between the specimen and objective lens; therefore, it is used to view large or living organisms that are too thick to be viewed with a compound microscope or to view larger objects that don't need as much magnification. The dissecting microscopes used in lab are binocular (meaning two oculars). The oculars are also moveable to allow you to adjust the distance between them to fit your eyes comfortably. Located on the rim of the ocular, you will see writing; the number 10X represents the magnification of the ocular. The model of dissecting scope used in class has the objective lenses housed in a protective chamber, so they can't be seen. To adjust the magnification, you will use the dial located on the top of the dissecting scope. There are also two dials located on either side of the arm. These dials are used to raise and lower the oculars to focus the image. Follow the instructions below to complete exercise.

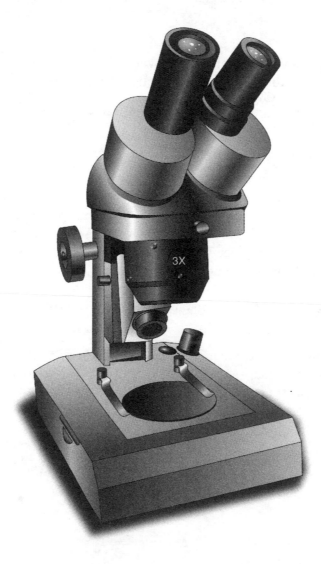

Figure 1: A dissecting microscope (Stereoscope).

1. Place a small piece of cork in a watchglass, and position it on the stage of the microscope. If cork is not available, place your finger on the stage and perform the experiment viewing your finger.

2. Next, adjust the oculars so that they are comfortable, and begin to focus on the cork, starting with the lowest power. The microscopes provided in class do not have a built-in light source; however, there is a rotating disk located under the stage that can be used to reflect light onto or away from the specimen. A secondary light source, such as a high-intensity lamp, may also be used to provide external light.

3. Once the cork is in focus at low power, adjust the setting of the objective lens to the highest magnification. You may need to adjust your light setting.

   a. Describe what you see: _It looks like a cork but zoomed in_

   b. What were you able to see with the dissecting scope that you could not see with your naked eye?
   You can see smaller details

Compound Light Microscope

Today, most microscopes are compound microscopes, and use two lenses for greater magnification. The upper lens is called the **ocular lens**, or eyepiece, and the lower lenses are called the **objective lenses**. When an image is formed, it is actually magnified twice. First, the image is formed at the bottom by the objective lens. Then, the image is projected through a tube and magnified again by the eyepiece (ocular) at the top. The image is always upside down, so what you see through the microscope shows up as the opposite of what you are doing. Any movement of the object also shows up in the opposite direction.

Parts of the Compound Light Microscope

Label the following parts of the compound microscope as your instructor explains them:

1. Ocular
2. Objective Lenses
3. Stage
4. Mechanical Stage
5. Mechanical Stage Adjustment
6. Condenser Lens
7. Arm
8. Coarse Adjustment
9. Fine Adjustment
10. Light Source
11. Base
12. Power Switch

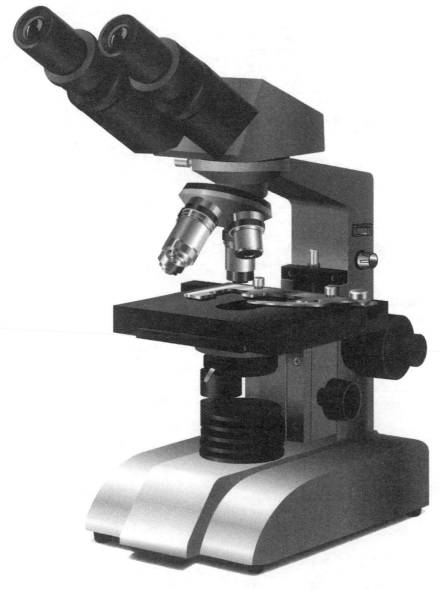

© bluedoor, LLC.

Figure 2: A dissecting microscope (Stereoscope).

How to Calculate Total Magnification

To calculate the total magnification of the image you are viewing through the microscope, you must know the magnification power of the objective lens and the ocular being used. The total magnification for the objective lenses is located on each side of the lenses, and on the rim of the oculars. To calculate total magnification, you multiply the magnification power of sthe ocular with the magnification power of the objective lens you are using. Fill in the table below to calculate the total magnification power for all the objectives.

	Magnification Power of Objective Lens	X	Magnification Power of Ocular	=	Total Magnification
Low Power	4	X	10	=	40
Medium Power	10	X	10	=	100
High Power	40	X	10	=	400
Oil Immersion	100	X	10	=	1600

Cleaning a Microscope

Always clean your microscope before and after each use. Follow these simple steps:

1. Wet a piece of lens tissue paper with a few drops of lens-cleaning solution.

2. Gently rub the wetted tissue paper on all the lenses (both oculars and all objective lenses), and the condenser lens found in the center of the stage. Never use anything other than lens tissue paper to clean the lenses of the microscope. Other items can scratch the glass.

Steps for Using and Focusing the Microscope

1. Plug in the microscope.

2. Switch it on (make sure the light works).

3. Lower the stage as far as it will go.

4. Rotate the objectives to the lowest setting (4X).

5. Put a slide on the stage.

6. Raise the stage up as high as it will go.

7. Look through the oculars while slowly moving the stage down (use coarse focus) until the specimen comes into view.

8. Use fine focus to get the clearest image.

Procedure 2

Orientation, Field of View, and Brightness

For this exercise, you will be observing a slide of the letter "e", using the objectives of the compound microscope with magnifications of 4X, 10X, and 40X. Before you start the exercise, look at and compare each of the objective lenses. You will see that with increased magnification, the diameter of the objective lens decreases. Also with increased magnification, the length of the objective lens increases and the working distance (the distance between the lens and the slide) decreases. Beneath the stage is a lens system, the condenser, and a 5-aperture disk diaphragm that operates like the iris of your eye to change the diameter of the beam of light. For maximum resolving power, the condenser focuses the light source on the specimen so that each of its points is evenly illuminated. The lever to the iris diaphragm on the condenser is used to open and close the condenser.

a. What happens to the field of view when the 5-aperture disk diaphragm is adjusted?

the full of view is clor wt
100 compund to 40

b. What do you think the diameter of the lens will do to the field of view?

It muly k wider or nncrowr

c. What do you think the diameter of the lens will do to the available light passing through the lens?

calton how brighk it is

Orientation

1. Place the slide on the stage, and focus the microscope using low magnification (4X).

a. What is the orientation of the letter "e" when viewed through the microscope (right side up, upside down, backwards, etc.)?

upside down

b. Using the stage adjustment to the mechanical stage, move the slide away from you. In which direction does the image move when viewed through the microscope?

opposite direction, so towards you

c. Again using the mechanical stage adjustment, move the slide to the left. In which direction does the image move when viewed through the microscope?

opposite, so to the right

Field of View

1. Once you have finished the exercise at low power (4X), center the image with the stage adjustment, and rotate the objective to the medium power (10X). You will hear a click when the objective is in place.

2. To get the image in focus, use the fine adjustment knob. (If you are unable to get the image in focus, rotate the stage down, switch back to low power, and start again.) Do not use the coarse adjustment while viewing under medium or high power; you will break the slide and the objective lens.

3. After the image is in focus at medium power, without moving the stage, rotate to the highest power objective (40X), and bring the image into focus. If you did not move the stage after you switched from medium to high magnification, the objective lens will not hit the slide. The objectives are parfocal, meaning that once the objective has been focused, you can rotate to another objective, and the image will remain in coarse focus, requiring only slight movement of the fine-adjust knob. You may have to adjust the disk diaphragm and the iris to properly illuminate the specimen.

a. How much of the letter "e" is in the field of view at high power?

not a lot

b. Why does the field of view change under different magnifications?

cause it zooms in and out

Brightness

Without changing any of the light settings, observe the light intensity at low (4X) and high (40X) magnification.

    a. Which magnification has the brightest image?

_100x_

    b. Why do you think the image is brighter for one of the magnifications?

it's the closest

Procedure 3

Depth of Field

For this exercise, you will view a slide of three overlapping colored threads. Specimens viewed with the microscope are of varying thicknesses, and a compound microscope can only focus on one plane of focus at a time. Understanding the concept of depth of field will help you visualize the structure within a thick section of tissue or a large single-celled organism.

   1. Place the slide on the stage, and focus it under low (4X) and then medium (10X) power.

   2. Once the slide is in focus at medium power, focus up and down to determine the relative position of the three colored threads.

    a. List the order of the threads as they appear on the slide. Top: _red_

    Middle: _blue_   Bottom: _yellow_

    b. At which magnification is it easiest to focus a specimen? Which is most difficult?

10x easiest

100x hardest

    c. How many threads can you clearly view at one time, and why?

1, it focuses on

each individually

Procedure 4

Preparing a "Wet Mount" of Cheek Epithelial Cells

1. Gently scrape the inside of your cheek with the flat side of a toothpick. (This scraping will collect some of your cheek cells for observation.)

2. Spread the cells on a microscope slide, add a small drop of water, and gently stir them together on the slide.

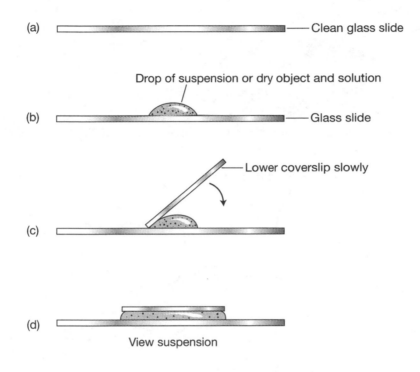

Figure 3: How to prepare a wet mount.

3. Now add a small drop of methylene blue (This will stain more than the cells, so be careful.) to the preparation, and stir again with the toothpick. Immediately after stirring, dispose of the toothpick in the trashcan labeled "Biohazardous Waste."

4. With your fingers, position the coverslip so that the bottom edge touches one side of the fluid on the slide. Then slowly lower the coverslip onto the preparation. If air is trapped under the coverslip, gently tap the top of the coverslip to push any air out, taking care not to push out your sample. Any excess fluid around the edge of the coverslip can be removed with filter paper. Before continuing, discard the used filter paper in the Biohazardous Waste trashcan.

5. View the slide under low, medium, and high power, and draw the views you see through the oculars in the following spaces provided.

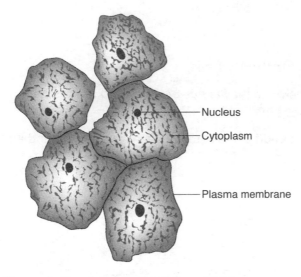

Figure 4: Cheek Epithelial Cells at 488X.

Observations at 40X magnification

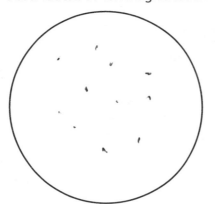

Observations at 100X magnification

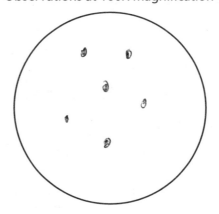

Observations at 400X magnification

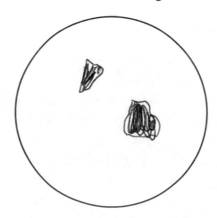

ඌ

a. Why does using **methylene blue** help you to view the nuclei of the cells better than the cytoplasm?

Cause the DNA in nucleus
to stant

Oil Immersion

Now, view the wet mounts you prepared of your cheek epithelial cells with the oil immersion objective (100X). Immersion oil has optical properties similar to glass, and will increase the resolving power and useful magnification.

1. First, bring the slide into focus with the high power objective (40X).

2. Next, rotate the objectives so that the light path is midway between the high power (40X) and oil immersion (100x) objectives.

3. Place a small drop of immersion oil onto the cover slip, using the circle of light as a reference point.

4. Rotate the objectives so that the oil immersion objective is in the oil.

5. Use the fine-adjust knob to focus the epithelial cells, and draw what you see in the space provided. You may also need to adjust the light source.

Observation at 1000X Magnification

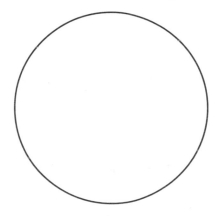

   a. What were you able to see under oil immersion that you could not see under high magnification?

_____

_____

   b. What are some of the limitations of microscopic observation?

_____

_____

   c. What difficulties, if any, did you encounter while using the microscope?

_____

_____

When this exercise is completed, **all slides and coverslips used for the wet mount should be discarded in the Biohazardous Waste trashcan. Do not leave the slides or coverslips in the sink.**

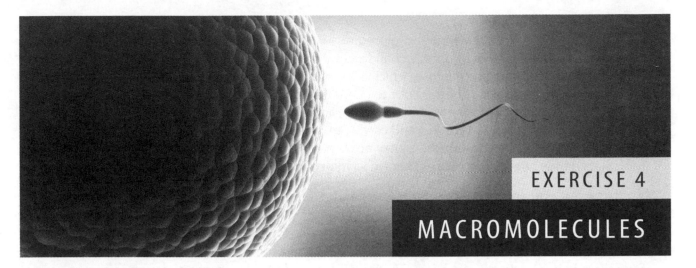

Carbohydrates

Objectives

After completing this exercise, you are expected to

1. Know the definition of monosaccharide, and name the monosaccharide components of sucrose and starch.

2. Define disaccharide, polysaccharide, and provide some examples.

3. Describe the tests that indicate the presence of simple sugars and starch.

4. Define hydrolysis.

5. Demonstrate, with examples, the process of hydrolysis of carbohydrates.

INTRODUCTION

For the most part, **carbohydrates** are composed of carbon (C), oxygen (O), and hydrogen (H). The **monosaccharides** (single sugars) are the simplest forms of carbohydrate molecules. There are many common monosaccharides, including fructose, galactose, and ribose. Glucose ($C_6H_{12}O_6$) is the most important monosaccharide, and the end product of photosynthesis in plants. Glucose is metabolized to produce ATP, whose energy can be used for cellular work.

On the other hand, a **disaccharide** is defined as two monosaccharides linked together. Disaccharides (double sugars) are also familiar. Maltose is a combination of two glucose molecules. Lactose, the milk sugar, consists of glucose and galactose. The table sugar commonly used, sucrose, is nothing but glucose and fructose. All of these are disaccharides.

When long chains of monosaccharide subunits are linked together, they constitute polysaccharides (many sugars). **Starch**, a polysaccharide composed of only glucose subunits, is a huge component in plants. Plants produce most of the carbohydrates that we (humans) consume. Starch is the plant's way of storing the glucose it makes during photosynthesis. Eating starch is the consumption of a plant's food reserves or energy storage. **Glycogen**, another form of polysaccharide, is used by animals to store glucose. Humans store small amounts of carbohydrates as glycogen in liver and muscle cells. However, excess carbohydrates are converted to lipids and are stored as fat.

Glucose subunits found in starch and glycogen are bonded differently. Glucose subunits bond together in yet a third form of polysaccharide, **cellulose**. While starch and glycogen are meant to be metabolized for energy, cellulose, which is the most abundant carbohydrate in the world, is a structural molecule that is designed not to be metabolized. Cellulose makes up the cell walls of plants. It is a primary component of dietary fiber, and is completely indigestible by most animals. Certain organisms, such as termites and cows, can only digest it with the help of bacteria, fungi, or protists. Organisms with digestive enzymes break down carbohydrates into their component monosaccharides through a process known as **hydrolysis**.

As discussed earlier in the chapter, disaccharides are simply two monosaccharides bonded together, while polysaccharides are composed of long chains of monosaccharides. Our bodies use **hydrolysis**, meaning, "to break with water," to break down the larger molecules. By breaking the bonds between sugars, we get smaller, more-usable molecules. The main example of hydrolysis in our bodies is digestion. The food we eat is bigger than one sugar molecule, and is too large to enter our cells. In our digestive tract, enzymes (proteins that speed up reactions), speed up hydrolysis. The products of hydrolysis are monosaccharides, which are small enough to be absorbed by our cells.

Activity A: Monosaccharides and Disaccharides

You will use **Benedict's reagent** as a general test for small sugars (monosaccharides and disaccharides). When this reagent is mixed with a solution containing mono- or disaccharides and then heated, a colored precipitate (solid material) forms. The precipitate may be yellow, green, orange, or red. If monosaccharides or disaccharides are not present, the reaction mixture remains clear. Benedict's reagent does not react with all small sugars. For example, sucrose gives a negative Benedict's reaction. Glucose will be used in this laboratory to demonstrate a positive Benedict's test. What should be used as a negative control? In this experiment, sucrose, a disaccharide, and starch, a polysaccharide, will be hydrolyzed. Heat and acid will be used to simulate the digestive process.

Procedure

1. Make a boiling-water bath by filling a beaker about half full of water and heating it on a hot plate. Place a few boiling chips in the beaker.

2. Label two test tubes 1 and 2.

3. Put 10 drops of glucose into Tube 1. Tube 1 is the positive control.

4. Tube 2 is the negative control. What substance goes in it? How much should be used?

5. Add 20 drops of Benedict's reagent to each tube.

6. Heat the tubes in a boiling-water bath for 5 minutes.

7. Remove the tubes from the water bath.

8. Allow the tubes to cool at room temperature for several minutes in the test tube rack while you go on to the next procedure.

9. Record your observations below:

Tube 1: _glucose turned dark/brown orange_

Tube 2: _DI Water, stayed the same_

Interpretation of Results

Describe a positive Benedict's test and the limitations of the test:

Activity B: Starch

The presence of starch is detected by using iodine reagent (I2KI-iodine potassium iodine). A dark blue color indicates the presence of starch. You will use a solution of potato starch to demonstrate a positive test.

Procedure

1. Label two test tubes 1 and 2.

2. Put 10 drops of starch in tube 1. This is the positive control.

3. Tube 2 is the negative control. What substance goes in it? How much should be used?

4. Put 3 or 4 drops of iodine reagent into each tube.

5. Record the results below:

Tube 1:

Tube 2:

Interpretation of Results

Give the limitations of this test:

Activity C: Hydrolysis of Carbohydrates

Disaccharides are composed of two monosaccharides linked together. Polysaccharides are long chains of monosaccharides. Hydrolysis is the process that turns large molecules into subunits by breaking down the linking bonds . Sucrose and starch will be hydrolyzed with heat and acid.

Procedure

1. Label 2 large test tubes: 1 starch and the other, sucrose.

2. Label 8 smaller test tubes from 1 through 8.

3. Pipette 10 milliliters (mL) of starch and 5 mL of 2N HCL (acid) into the large tube labeled "starch." (10 drops = 1 mL)

4. Pipette 10 mL of sucrose and 2 mL of 2N HCL into the large tube labeled "sucrose".

5. Mix each solution by swirling gently.

6. Place 1 dropper (a pipette full) of sucrose/HCL solution into the tube labeled 1.

7. Using a clean pipette, place 1 dropper of starch/HCL solution into the tube labeled 3.

8. Place another dropper of starch/HCL solution into the tube labeled 4.

9. Place the larger test tubes labeled "starch" and "sucrose" into the boiling-water bath. Note the time.

10. After 2 to 3 minutes, draw 1 dropper of solution from the sucrose/HCL tube (in water bath) and place it into the tube labeled 2.

11. At the 5-minute mark, draw 1 dropper of solution from the starch/HCL tube (in water bath) and place it into the tube labeled 5.

12. Put a second dropper of this same solution into the tube labeled 6.

13. Wait 10 minutes more. Place 1 dropper of solution from the starch/HCL tube into tube "7" and another dropper of this solution into tube 8.

14. Add 2 droppers of Benedict's reagent to the tubes labeled 1, 2, 3, 5, and 7. Place these tubes into the water bath for an additional 5 minutes.

15. Add 3 to 4 drops of iodine reagent to the tubes labeled 4, 6, and 8. Do not place these into the water bath.

16. Remove tubes 1, 2, 3, 5, and 7 from the water bath, and allow them to cool for 5 minutes. Record the results in the following table. * These times are the initial times spent in the water bath. The 5 minutes that tubes 1, 2, 3, 5, and 7 spent in the water bath were for the reaction with the Benedict's reagent.

	Tube Number							
	Sucrose		Starch					
	1	2	3	4	5	6	7	8
Time (min)	0	2-3	0	0	5	5	15	15
Benedict's reagent								
Iodine reagent								

Table 4.1: Hydrolysis of carbohydrates data table.

Interpretation of Results

a. Explain the results you obtained using the Benedict's test on both the starch and sucrose solutions:

_____

_____

b. Explain the results you obtained using the iodine reagent test on both the sucrose and starch solutions:

_____

_____

c. Why does hydrolysis of starch take longer than hydrolysis of sucrose?

_____

_____

Objectives

Activity D: Lipids

After completing this exercise you will be able to

1. Define lipids and provide examples.

2. Describe the test indicating the presence of lipids.

INTRODUCTION

Lipids are compounds that contain mostly carbon and hydrogen, grouped together because of their insolubility in water. The lipids that will be considered in this laboratory are fats and oils, generally used as storage molecules in both plants and animals. After ingestion, excess food is converted by the body into fat. Fat is stored as adipose tissue until food intake is lower than metabolic needs. Then fat is metabolized to generate ATP, whose energy can be used for cellular work. Plants store fat in seeds. The seeds contain a reservoir of fat that can be metabolized for energy. Corn oil, olive oil, peanut oil, sunflower oil, and the like are obtained by pressing the seeds.

You will use the **paper test** to indicate the presence of lipids in various foods.

Procedure

1. Obtain a small square of brown paper. Write "oil" on one half and "water" on the other.

2. Put a tiny drop of salad oil on the half of the paper labeled oil. Rub it gently with your fingertip.

3. As a negative control, put a tiny drop of water on the half of the paper labeled water. Rub it gently with a different fingertip to avoid contamination.

4. Allow the spots to dry.

5. When the spots are dry, hold the paper up to the light.

Interpretations of Results

Describe a positive test for lipids:

What are the limitations of this test?

Activity E: Proteins

Objectives

After completing the following exercise, you should be able to

1. Define and give examples of protein.

2. Explain the relationship between the structure and function of a protein.

3. Describe the test that indicates the presence of protein.

INTRODUCTION

The structure of a **protein** is determined by the amino acid subunits that make up the molecule. There are 20 different naturally occurring amino acids, but each protein molecule has a unique sequence. Fairly tight bonds link amino acids, and side groups that are part of the amino acids also interact with each other to help shape the molecule. The shape of a protein is the key to its purpose, as proteins work by selectively binding to other molecules.

You will use biuret reagent as a test for proteins. This reagent, which is blue, reacts with proteins to give a light violet or lavender color. You will use a solution of egg albumin (a protein extracted from egg whites) to demonstrate a positive biuret test. What negative control should be used for this test?

Procedure

1. Get two test tubes and label them 1 and 2.

2. Put 20 drops of egg albumin into tube 1.

3. Tube 2 is the control. What substance goes in it? How much should be used?

4. Put 10 drops of biuret reagent into each tube, and swirl gently to mix.

5. After 2 minutes, record the color in each tube.

Tube 1: (egg albumin):

Tube 2: (negative control):

Interpretation of Results

Describe a positive biuret test:

What are the limitations of this test?

Procedure

Test the foods and beverage provided in lab for simple sugars, starch, lipids, and proteins. Separate into groups, and run the four tests previously described in lab on each of the items provided by your lab instructor. Then share your results with the class.

The following procedure should be used when running run tests on solid foods (except the lipid test).

1. Use a razor blade to mince up the sample (a 1 cm-sized sample, about the size of a pea, will be adequate).

2. After the sample has been minced, place it into a test tube with 10 mL of distilled water, and mix vigorously for approximately 1 minute.

3. Then add the recommended amount of reagent for the test you are trying to run.

Be sure to clean all equipment (razor blade and cutting board) after each use to avoid cross contamination.

Benedict's Test (simple sugars)

Mix 10 drops of sample with 20 drops of Benedict's reagent in a test tube, and heat for 5 minutes in a boiling-water bath. Then remove the tube, allow the sample to cool, and determine the results.

Iodine Test (starch)

Mix 10 drops of sample with 4 or 5 drops of iodine reagent in a test tube, and determine the results.

Paper Test (lipid)

Place a small drop of the sample on the brown paper provided in lab, gently rub it in, and then allow it to dry. If the sample is a solid object (for example, a peanut) mince or crush it up as finely as possible, then rub it on the brown paper.

Biuret Test (protein)

Mix 10 drops of sample and 10 drops of biuret reagent in a test tube, and determine the results.

Record your results, and the class results, in the table provided.

Table 4.2: Food and beverage data table.

Sample	Benedict's (sugar)	Iodine (starch)	Paper (lipid)	Biruet (protein)
glucose	+	X	X	X
starch	X	+	X	X
albumin	X	X	X	+
oil	X	X	X +	X
A	+	+	−	+
B	+	−	−	+
C	+	−	+	+

Interpretation of Results

1. Were any of the results different from what you expected to find?

   _____

   _____

2. Did you have any false-negative results (meaning, the food tested contained a molecule, but the test results were negative)? What are some factors that might result in a false-negative test?

   _____

   _____

3. Why might a plant storage organ (fruit or tuber) contain both starch and sugar?

   _____

   _____

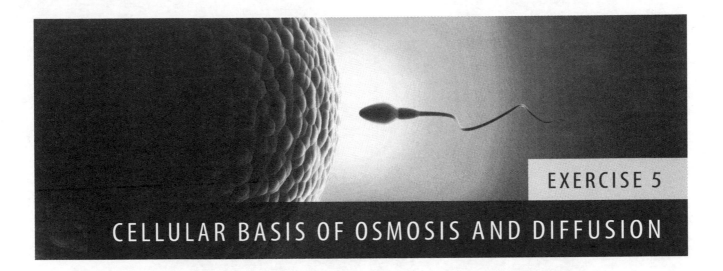

CELLULAR BASIS OF OSMOSIS AND DIFFUSION

Objectives

The objectives of this exercise are to understand the process of osmosis and diffusion, to experimentally determine the tonicity of unknown solutions, to experimentally observe diffusion of a gas, and to experimentally observe osmosis.

INTRODUCTION

The body is constantly trying to achieve **homeostasis** by moving substances across the cellular membrane of cells. Ions and organic compounds, such as sugars and amino acids, must enter the cell, whereas waste products must leave the cell. The regulation of movement of such materials across the cell membrane and across membranes of the cellular organelles occurs because these membranes are **selectively permeable;** they only allow certain molecules across.

The proper functioning of the cell depends on the physical and chemical integrity of the membrane. **Figure 5.1** shows the phospholipid bilayer of the membrane allowing certain particles, such as small, uncharged polar molecules and hydrophobic molecules, to pass through while large, uncharged polar molecules and ions are rejected. Membrane permeability depends on the solubility and size of the molecules trying to penetrate the membrane. Large particles are submerged in the membrane and form a vesicle or vacuole that can pass in or out of the cell. Small molecules diffuse through the spaces between lipid molecules. Other molecules bind with proteins in the membrane and are transported in or out of the cell. The movement of materials across the cell's membrane can be achieved by either **active transport**, which requires energy, or by **passive transport**, which does not require energy. Passive transport occurs only if the membrane is permeable to the substance.

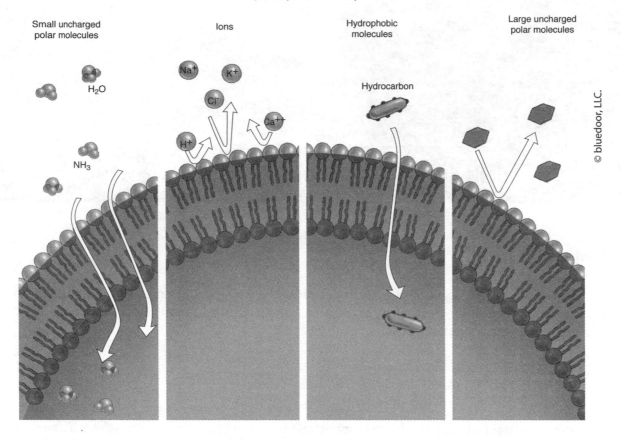

Lipid Bilayer Permeability

Small uncharged polar molecules

Ions

Hydrophobic molecules

Large uncharged polar molecules

H₂O

NH₃

Na⁺   K⁺

Cl⁻

Ca⁺⁺

H⁺

Hydrocarbon

© bluedoor, LLC.

Figure 1: The selective permeability of the plasma membrane.

Diffusion is the movement of molecules from an area of high concentration to an area of low concentration. **Osmosis** is a specialized type of diffusion in which water moves from high water content (low solute) to low water content (high solute). Three terms are used to describe the two solutions separated by a selectively permeable membrane: **hypertonic, hypotonic**, and **isotonic**. If a cell is in a **hypertonic** solution, the concentration of the solute is greater in the solution than in the cell. Water will diffuse out of the cell, and the cell will crenate, or shrink, in size. When a cell is placed in a **hypotonic** solution, the concentration of the solute is lower in the solution than in the cell; therefore, water flows into the cell causing it to fill up and lyse, or burst. When the two concentrations are equal on both sides of the membrane, the solutions are called isotonic (see top of **Figure 5.2**).

Plant cells are somewhat different from animal cells. There are three features of plant cells that distinguish them from animal cells: **a cell wall, chloroplasts, and a vacuole**. The rigid cell wall of plants is composed of cellulose and other polysaccharides. Within the wall, and usually pressed up against it, is the plasma membrane. As water flows into a plant cell, the **cytoplasm** (all of the material enclosed by the cell wall, excluding the nucleus) expands until it reaches the cell wall. The cell wall restricts the expansion of the cell, which results in **turgor pressure**. Turgor pressure is the pressure of the cytoplasm on the cell wall due to the uptake of water. High turgor pressure prevents more water from entering the cell. As water leaves the cell, the plasma membrane and its contents shrink, but the cell wall remains the same (see bottom of **Figure 5.2**).

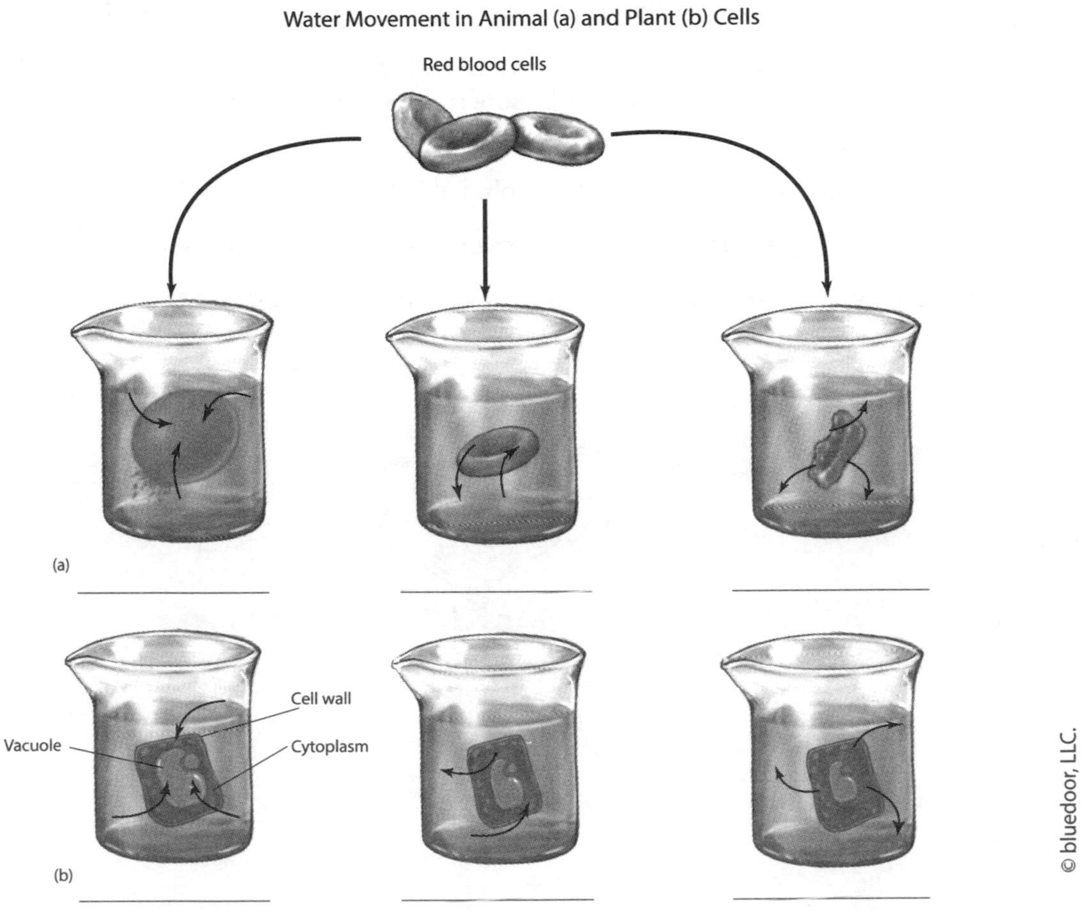

Water Movement in Animal (a) and Plant (b) Cells

Red blood cells

(a) _____ _____ _____

Vacuole — Cell wall
Cytoplasm

(b) _____ _____ _____

© bluedoor, LLC.

Figure 2: Animal cells and plant cells in solutions of varying tonicity.

You have probably seen diffusion at work many times if you have ever stayed in the swimming pool or bath long enough for your fingers to wrinkle. The dermal cells in your fingers are being exposed to a hypotonic solution and, in return, swell, while the connective tissue stays the same size. The cells in your fingers take in so much water they eventually lyse, causing your fingers to wrinkle.

Procedure 1

You will now observe the process of osmosis using an osmometer in which a dialysis membrane mimics the cell membrane. The dialysis membrane is made of cellulose and, like the cell membrane, allows some substances to readily pass through the membrane, while other substances do not, depending on their size.

1. Obtain a double-end thistle tube.

   Exercise caution when handling thistle tubes. They break very easily!

2. Slightly dampen the dialysis membrane with water, being sure not to soak it for too long. Soak a dialysis membrane disc in water for a few minutes. Cover one end of the thistle tube with the dialysis membrane, and secure it with a rubber band. Make sure the membrane over the thistle tube opening is taut by pulling its free edges, while it's still damp.

3. Attach the metal clamp to the side of the reservoir, and insert the thistle tube into the clamp.

4. Fill the entire bell (at the bottom of the tube) of the thistle tube and 1 inch of the stem with the 35% sucrose solution + neutral red. Be sure to wipe away any spilled solution from the tube.

5. With a grease pencil, mark the level of the solution in the stem of the tube.

6. Fill the reservoir/beaker with water until it covers the bell of the thistle tube.

7. Observe the height of the fluid in the stem tube every 15 minutes.

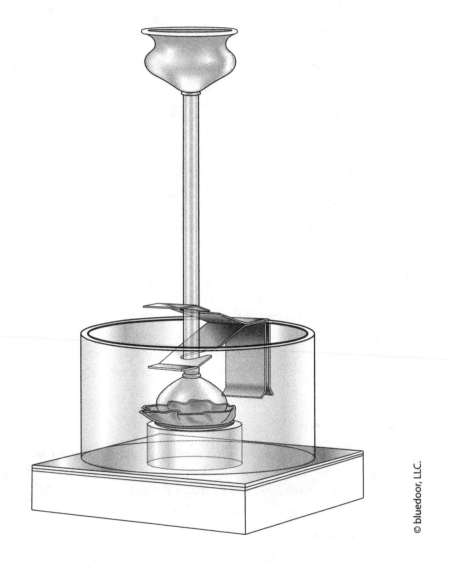

Figure 3: Setup of an osmometer.

Record your data in the chart below.

Time	Elapsed Time(min)	Height
	0	
	15	
	30	
	45	
	60	

1. Is the solution in the thistle tube hypertonic, hypotonic, or isotonic to the water in the beaker? Explain.

_____

_____

2. Why was a dialysis membrane used for this experiment?

_____

_____

Procedure 2

The diffusion of gas is very important in many physiological processes. Oxygen from the air is diffused from the air, across tissues, and into the lungs of humans and other animals. The same process releases carbon dioxide, diffusing across the lung tissues and being released into the air. Let's take a look at how diffusion of a gas occurs.

1. Remain seated at your lab bench; your instructor will assign row numbers.

2. Your instructor will light incense at the front of the room.

3. Record the time the incense is lit; this is time zero.

4. Record the time in minutes and seconds (hr:min:sec) when the incense is detected by each row.

5. Once the seventh row detects the incense, the odor has diffused into the air throughout the room.

6. Record your data in the chart below.

Row #	Time detected	Amount of time to detect
0	(time zero)	(time deficit-time zero)
1		
2		
3		
4		
5		
6		
7		

7. Why is diffusion of gases important in plants also?

_____

_____

_____

8. Plot a graph below that represents the distance (row) vs. the time it took to detect the incense.

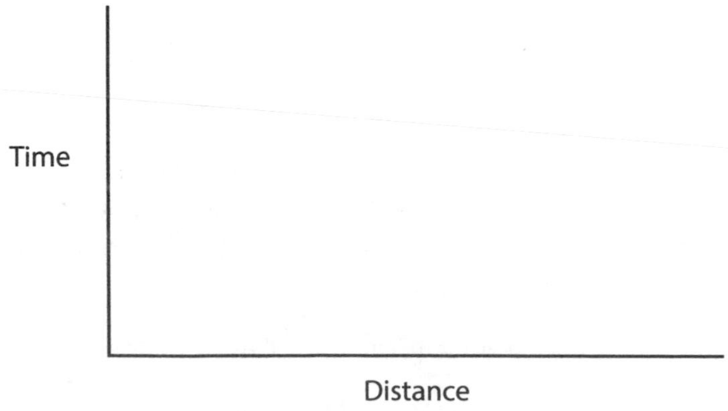

Time

Distance

Procedure 3

Erythrocytes, or red blood cells, are naturally flattened and pinched to form a biconcave disk. It is very important to keep them isotonic to their solution, or they will be destroyed. Carbon dioxide and oxygen diffuse across the erythrocyte membrane, allowing them to carry out gas exchange. In this experiment, you will observe what happens to erythrocytes when they are subject to solutions that are not isotonic.

1. Obtain 4 clean slides.

2. Place a drop of ox blood on one slide, cover it with a coverslip, and observe the size and shape of the erythrocytes, using a compound microscope. Note: It is important that you use a small drop of blood, otherwise the erythrocytes will not be visible.

3. Obtain the 3 salt solutions (0%, 5%, 0.85%).

4. Place 1 drop of the 0% solution and 1 drop of the ox blood on a clean slide, and cover with a coverslip.

5. Place the slide on the microscope stage.

6. Observe the shape of the cells once they come into contact with the solution.

7. Repeat the procedure 2 more times using the 5% and 0.85% solutions.

Draw what you saw when observing the ox blood in Step 2.

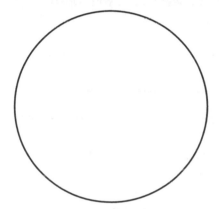

Draw what you saw once you added the 0% solution.

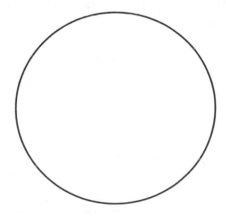

Draw what you saw after adding the 0.85% solution.

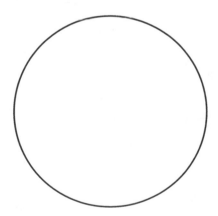

Draw what you saw after adding the 5% solution.

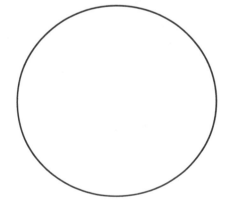

8. Which solution was hypertonic? How could you tell?

_____

_____

_____

9. Which solution was hypotonic? How could you tell?

_____

_____

_____

10. Which solution was isotonic? How could you tell?

_____

_____

_____

11. Was there an immediate change in shape/size of the erythrocytes once you added the solution?

_____

_____

_____

12. Why is it important for hospitals, when administering an IV, to know the isotonic point of human cells?

_____

_____

_____

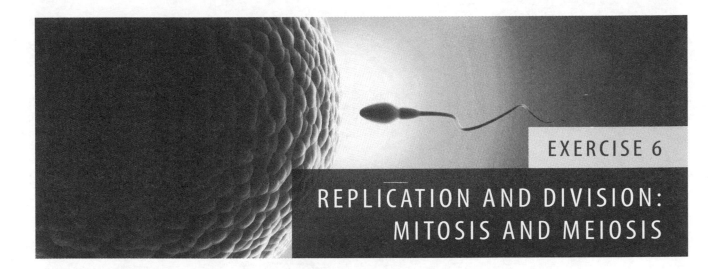

REPLICATION AND DIVISION: MITOSIS AND MEIOSIS

Objectives

The objectives of this exercise are to represent visually each of the four phases of mitosis, to understand the fundamental differences between mitosis and meiosis, to identify the stage of mitosis and or meiosis that a cell is undergoing, and to make slides of cells undergoing mitosis.

INTRODUCTION

Onion root tips are very effective for viewing real-life cell division. In this next part of your study, you will prepare your own slides of onion root tips, stain them to highlight the nuclear materials, and view the many different stages of mitosis that occur in one root tip.

Cells contain many **organelles**, each having a specific function relating to the overall purpose of the cell. **Reproduction** means to produce a new generation of cells. The **nucleus** contains the **hereditary** material, **deoxyribonucleic acid** (**DNA**), which contains the instructions to make proteins required by all cells to function properly. During the growth phase of the cell (interphase) the DNA is difficult to observe under the microscope because it is not condensed. The DNA molecules are thread-like, with proteins attached to them, and are called chromosomes. The attached proteins are involved in the duplication of the chromosome, a process which occurs during the growth phase of the cell. At the end of interphase (not part of mitosis or meiosis), each chromosome consists of two **sister chromatids** attached at their central regions, called **centromeres**. As the cell moves into its reproductive phase (cell division: **prophase**, **metaphase**, **anaphase**, and **telophase**), the DNA starts to condense and becomes easy to stain and observe as it goes through the stages of cell division.

The cells in our body are not all at the same stage of mitosis and meiosis at the same time. Each cell undergoes replication or reduction at a different rate. For instance, our kidneys are made up of thousands of cells, but each cell may be undergoing a different stage of mitosis.

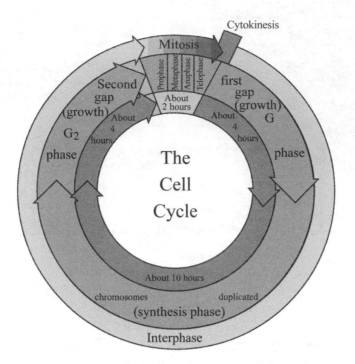

Figure 1: The cell cycle.

Mitosis in Detail

Somatic cells divide by a process called mitosis. Mitosis has four stages: prophase, metaphase, anaphase, and telophase. The chromosomes have already condensed and replicated during interphase.

Prophase: Chromosomes are visible within the nuclear membrane. Each contains two sister chromatids joined at the **centromere**. Near the nucleus are two bundles called **centrioles**, placed at right angles to each other. At the beginning of the division phase of the cell, the centrioles start to separate and move to opposite poles of the cell. As they move, they form spindle fibers between them, which guide the chromosomes later. The nuclear membrane begins to break down.

Metaphase: Spindle fibers attach to the chromosomes at their centromeres and drag the chromosomes to the equator of the cell.

Anaphase: The two sister chromatids separate, one being dragged by the spindle fibers in the direction of one centriole, the other in the opposite direction to the other centriole. Now each sister chromatid is a single chromosome again.

Telophase: When the chromosomes reach the centrioles, the spindle fibers break down, and the chromosomes return to their thread-like form. A nuclear membrane forms around each set of chromosomes, leaving the centriole outside. Now each nucleus contains a set of chromosomes that are identical in number and composition to that of the parent cell. The cytoplasm is divided between the two nuclei, resulting in two identical cells, each containing identical chromosomes and enough cytoplasm to start the growth and reproduction cycle again.

Procedure

Now, as part of your project, you will study cell division in the onion root. We can take actively growing roots of an onion and arrest the growing process. In doing so, we will be able to see cells that are in each of the four phases of mitosis by making a microscope slide of the root tip.

1. Place a drop of aceto-orcein stain on a clean microscope slide.

2. Using forceps, take a root tip from your onion that was previously fixed in a solution of concentrated HCl and ethanol, then placed in distilled water.

3. Place the root tip in the stain.

4. Carefully remove all but the very tip of the root (it's usually somewhat bulbous).

5. Use the dissecting needle to tease the root tip apart (be gentle here!). Carefully place a coverslip on the slide, and lightly tap it with the tip of a ballpoint pen or your fingernail to disperse the cells.

6. Look to see if the cells are still in clumps. If so, again tap on the coverslip until the cells are dispersed.

7. Cover the slide with a paper towel, and press down evenly to flatten the cells. DO NOT PRESS TOO HARD OR YOU WILL BREAK THE SLIDE!

8. Use the compound microscope to view your cells. Start by using the low-power objective, and work your way up to the high-power objective. [Hint: If you have forgotten how to do this, go back to the module on visual observation, and review the process.]

9. Locate each of the four phases of mitosis that are described below.

10. Fill in Table 1 by looking at four different fields of view. You may have to estimate the number of cells found for certain phases.

Table 1: The number of cells in each of the four stages of mitosis through four fields of view.

Phase	Field of view 1	Field of view 2	Field of view 3	Field of view 4
Prophase				
Metaphase				
Anaphase				
Telophase				

Everything you see through the ocular is in one **field of view**. If you were to move your slide, you would be looking at a different field of view. You will have looked at four different fields of view if you have moved your slide 3 times after focusing (the first field of view was when you focused). [Hint: To review, look back at 'fields of view' and why they are important in your visual observation lab.]

Was your onion root tip actively growing? Why do you know this?

_____

In what area of the root tip do you see most cell division?

_____

Can you see the root tip cap? What do you think its function is? Would you expect many dividing cells in this area?

_____

_____

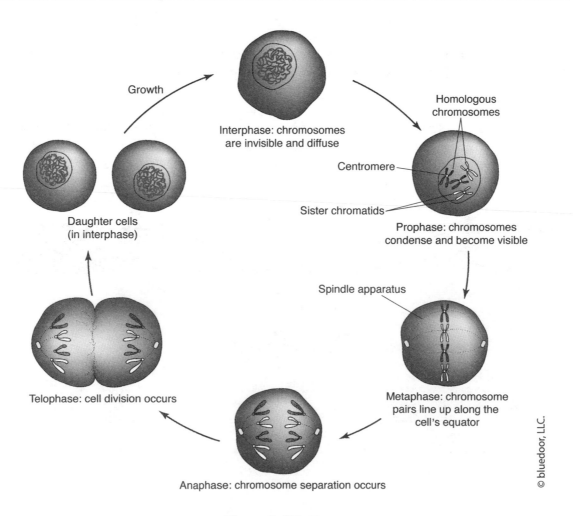

Figure 2: Mitosis.

Mitosis results in two identical cells. What does this mean in terms of the number of chromosomes in each new cell?

_____

_____

The word "clone" means identical in every way. Are cells that result from mitosis clones?

_____

Identical twins result because of complete separation of two cells at the first mitotic division after fertilization. Are twins clones?

_____

_____

Meiosis

Only sex cells undergo meiotic division. So although we cannot use onions in this next experiment, it is important that you also understand the process of meiosis.

Meiosis is the process that results in the formation of **sex cells**, or **gametes**. Meiosis divides the chromosomes not once, but twice. **Diploid** cells have two of each type of chromosome, and they are called **homologous** chromosomes (*homo* means alike). It is the first step in **sexual reproduction**, and results in gametes that contain one-half (1n) of the complement of chromosomes required to make an individual (2n). Another interesting part of meiosis is the ability of chromosomal material to be exchanged between chromosomes, resulting in **variation**. This process is called **crossing over**. Meiosis has two distinct stages: Meiosis I and Meiosis II.

> **Interphase:** each cell contains pairs of homologous chromosomes, one from each parent. During interphase, each chromosome replicates in a manner similar to that of mitosis. Two centrioles are required. **Interphase, while not a phase of meiosis, is necessary for meiosis to take place.**

Meiosis I

> **Prophase I:** Chromosomes begin to condense, and homologous chromosomes, each made up of two chromatids, pair up. **Crossing over**, where chromosomal material is exchanged between chromosomes, occurs only during Prophase I. Each centriole starts to move to the poles, and the nuclear membrane breaks down.

> **Metaphase I:** The homologous chromosomes move to the equator of the cell.

> **Anaphase I:** The homologous chromosomes (each contains sister chromatids) separates and begins to migrate toward the centrioles.

> **Telophase I:** Each chromosome is near its centriole. Nuclear membrane forms, and cytoplasmic division occurs to produce two cells.

Second Division

Prophase II: Centrioles migrate to the poles. Nuclear membrane breaks down.

Metaphase II: The chromosomes align on the equator of the cell.

Anaphase II: Sister chromatids separate and move to poles.

Telophase II: Chromosomes pile close to the centriole and the nuclear membrane. Cytoplasmic division occurs, resulting in a total of four nuclei.

Which part of meiosis is most similar to mitosis? _____

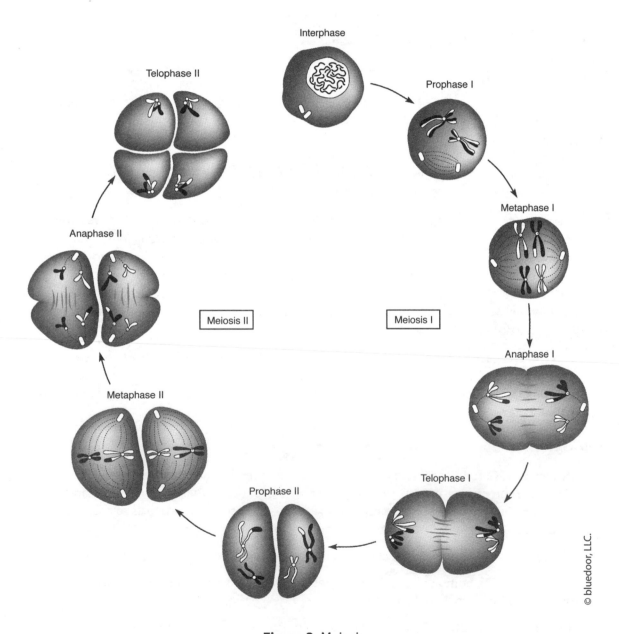

Interphase

Prophase I

Metaphase I

Anaphase I

Telophase I

Prophase II

Metaphase II

Anaphase II

Telophase II

Meiosis II

Meiosis I

© bluedoor, LLC.

Figure 3: Meiosis.

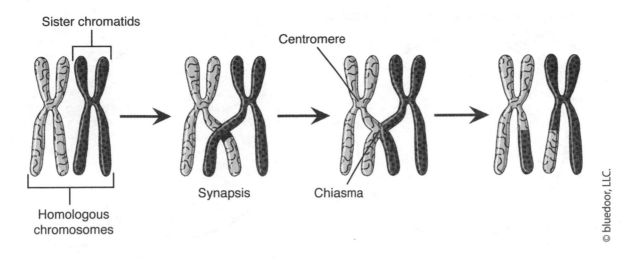

Sister chromatids

Centromere

Synapsis

Chiasma

Homologous chromosomes

© bluedoor, LLC.

Figure 4: Crossing over.

Obtain some prepared slides of meiosis in plant cells and become familiar with each stage. If you are not sure about what you are looking at on the slide, use your simulated chromosomes to clarify the stage you see.

Ask your TA for slides of cells from different tissues and see if you can identify the stage of meiosis and why you know which stage it is.

Once you are completely sure you understand meiosis, draw the stages you saw.

Mitotically dividing cells have a full complement of chromosomes, and are called diploid cells. Knowing the amount of chromosomal material in the nuclei that forms after meiosis, what does "haploid" mean?

_____

_____

_____

Use these spaces to draw the stages of meiosis.

No crossing over occurs in mitosis, but does in meiosis. Define crossing over and what results from this process.

_____

_____

_____

_____

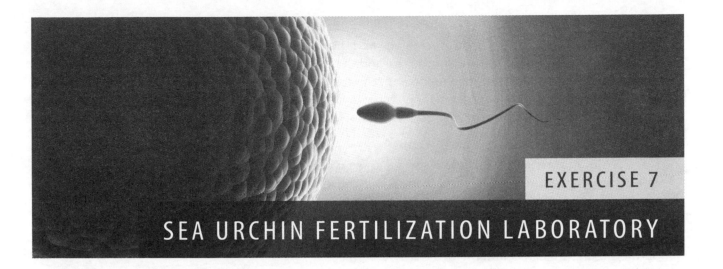

EXERCISE 7

SEA URCHIN FERTILIZATION LABORATORY

Objectives

In this laboratory, you will learn about the process of fertilization that occurs in sea urchins, and you will study their physiology. In addition, you will examine the embryo development processes known as **embryogenesis** and observe the different larval stages of the sea urchin prior to becoming an adult.

INTRODUCTION

Known as the "pin cushions" of the sea, sea urchins are those fearsome-looking **invertebrates** that belong to the phylum Echinodermata, meaning spiny skin. These animals are exclusively marine **benthic** dwellers, which help to maintain an important environmental balance within the marine ecosystem.

Define the following;

Invertebrate:

_____

Benthic:

_____

Intertidal:

_____

Sea urchins are a group of echinoderms in the class, Echinoidea, Greek for "like a hedgehog". Unique to these sea creatures is their body structure development, which can be described as pentamerous radial symmetry. Sea urchin bodies can be divided into five parts arranged around a central point, or axis. The internal skeleton of the sea urchin, or test, is a calcareous structure with ossicles, raised calcareous protrusions, fused together to form ambulacral plates. These plates give the sea urchin its shape, which is generally circular or oval.

The most noticeable attribute of the echinoids, and their namesake, are the sharp spines emanating from their test. Sea urchin spines range in size and sharpness, but, in general, they are hollow, brittle structures that are designed for defense and movement. If you were to accidentally step on or handle a sea urchin in a careless manner, you would learn a painful lesson, as the spines contain a toxin, and they cannot be removed from your skin. The spines will eventually dissolve, but not without some discomfort.

There are approximately 700 different species of sea urchins widely distributed throughout the world's oceans. Benthic dwellers, they can be found in intertidal areas to the deep oceans. They are adapted to living on hard substrates, such as rocks, and corals, and some species will burrow beneath the sand. Sea urchins range in size from 2 - 4 inches, with some Indo-Pacific species reaching up to a foot in diameter. Echinoids come in a wide variety of colors, including brown, black, purple, green, white, red, and multicolors.

Sea urchins are omnivores, feeding on all types of organic material, living and dead. They play an especially important part in maintaining a balance within the coral reef ecosystem by keeping algae growth from proliferating out of control.

What would happen if sea urchins were removed from the environment by over-fishing, disease, or predation?

_____

_____

Sea Urchin Anatomy

Sea urchin body structure can be divided into two hemispheres: **aboral** and **oral** regions. Regular echinoids, such as the Long-spined black urchin (Diadema antillarum) have their oral region, or mouth, on the bottom side, or the side facing the substrate. The anus, aboral region, is located on their top side, or the side that is exposed to the surface. Irregular urchins, which include sand dollars, heart urchins, and cake urchins, have both their aboral and oral regions located on their underside facing the substrate.

In the oral region, sea urchins have a highly developed feeding apparatus called **Aristotle's Lantern**. The lantern can be protracted and retracted through the mouth by special muscles, and is an effective chewing mechanism.

Sea urchins are grazers, and, despite their appearance, are quite mobile. Echinoid **spines** are movable, and, in addition to being a defense mechanism, provide locomotion by pushing the urchin along the sea floor. In the Caribbean, for example, sea urchins find shelter during the day within coral crevasses, and at night will emerge from hiding and move about the reef foraging for food. Special tube feet, or **podia**, are used to attach the urchin to hard substrates. Part of the echinoid's water vascular system, the tube feet are extended by filling with water, and the ends are raised, creating a suction effect that holds the animal in place. The podia are extruded through tiny **perforations** on the **ambulacral plates**. The **interambulacrum** does not contain these perforations.

Label the parts of the following diagrams:

1. Mouth
2. Anus
3. Ambularcrum
4. Periproct
5. Test
6. Podia perforation
7. Aristotle's Lantern
8. Gonads
9. Gonopore
10. Peristomal membrane
11. Genital Plates
12. Interambulacrum
13. Anterior ambulacra
14. Posterior ambulacra
15. Peristome
16. Plate of test

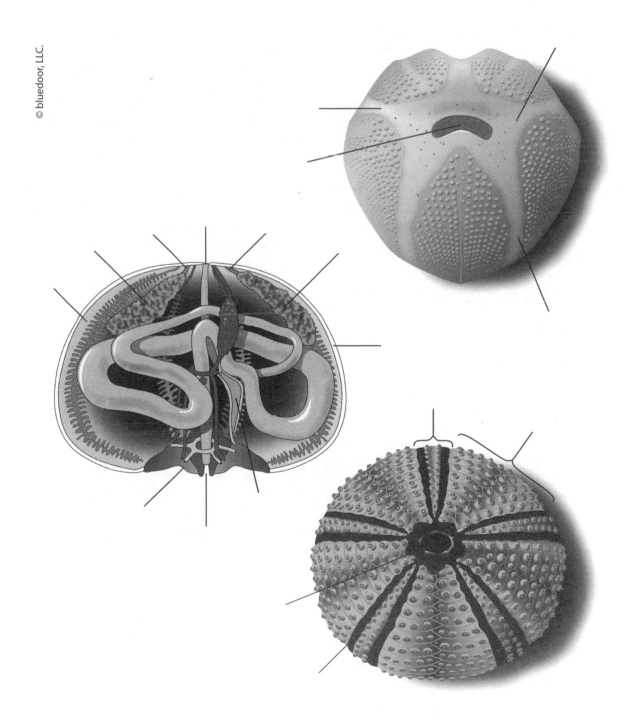

Reproduction

Sea urchings are sexually distinct, or **dioecious**. The term "dioecious" means that there are male sea urchins and female sea urchins, as opposed to an organism containing both male and female characteristics. Given this, however, sea urchins are not sexually dimorphic, meaning there is no structural difference between the sexes. Most sea urchins reproduce by spawning; females and males release their eggs and sperm into the water. This type of fertilization is known as "external fertilization" because it occurs outside the body cavity, whereas, in mammals, fertilization occurs inside the body (internal fertilization).

Sea urchin fertilization takes place in the water column. Male and female gametes are released by contractions in the muscle layers of the gonads. Short **gonoducts** extend aborally from each gonad and open through a **gonopore** located on one of the 5 **gonadal plates**. If an organism, such as some echinoids, uses the strategy above, also known as broadcast spawning, it must produce very large numbers of young in order for the species to survive. Embryos become part of the **plankton** column, which is a food source for many marine organisms. Millions of embryos must be formed in order for a few to survive. Spawning occurs seasonally. For urchins living in temperate areas, spawning occurs in spring and early summer.

Some species of sea urchins are brooders, meaning they do not release their young into the water column, but retain their eggs on the **periostome** (tissues and structures around the mouth), or around the **perioproct** (a small circular membrane containing the anus, usually located in the center), keeping the eggs in place with their spines. Species of echinoids that are brooders do not have to produce as many young.

Why do you think brooders produce fewer young than urchins who are broadcast spawners?

_____

_____

Define Plankton:

_____

_____

Sea urchins are great organisms for studying the mechanisms of fertilization and embryology. Many characteristics of their fertilization process can be contrasted and compared with those of mammals. Listed below are some differences and similarities between sea urchins and mammals, such as humans.

Similarities between Sea Urchins and Mammals

- Sperm cells are the smallest cells produced by the body. Evolution favored the production of numerous tiny sperm because the more sperm produced by the males, the better the chance the egg will be fertilized. The more lottery tickets you have, the better the chance of winning the big prize!

- Sea urchin eggs and human eggs release a chemical signal that the sperm uses to locate them.

- Sea urchins and mammals have a mechanism to allow only one sperm to fertilize the egg, and block other sperm from trying to fertilize the same egg. This mechanism is called "Block to Polyspermy".

Block to Polyspermy

Once fertilization has occurred, a fertilization membrane is formed, working as a physical barrier to other upcoming sperm. This barrier lifts up, first on the egg's surface, at the site where the sperm entered. This process involves the depolarization of the egg's cell membrane with calcium ions that create electrical charges to block other sperm from entering the egg, and activates the release of cortical granules around the egg's surface. These cortical granules contain enzymes that degrade the fertilization receptor protein and harden the cell membrane.

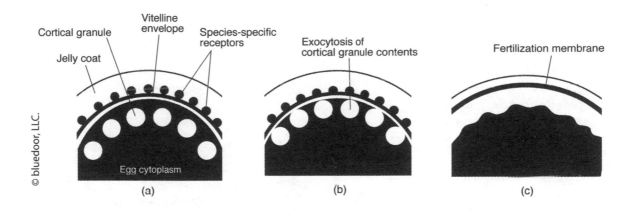

Differences between Sea Urchins and Mammals

- External fertilization is observed in sea urchins, whereas internal fertilization is used in mammals.

- Urchins produce thousands of eggs, whereas humans produce only one egg (oocyte) that when fertilized becomes a zygote that will grow inside the female's uterus.

- Once sea urchins release their gametes, they move on to feeding or other normal activities and do not worry about their progeny at all. Humans and other mammals, on the other hand, will take care of their offspring sometimes up to 30 or 40 years!

Experimental Procedure

Today you will see the process of fertilization in vivo thanks to the sea urchins provided for you in this laboratory. You will also see some of the developmental stages of the young larva prior to being an adult sea urchin. Sea urchins can be induced to release gametes by injecting them with a solution of potassium chloride (KCL).

WARNING: KCL should be handled carefully. Let your instructor help you with this section to avoid accidents.

Note: Keep in mind that sea urchins have a nervous system, and they are capable of feeling sensations and pain, so please handle them properly. When you finish the lab, put the sea urchins in the seawater container labeled "Used". The used sea urchins will be returned back to the sea afterwards.

The instructor will demonstrate this procedure to the class. The steps are as followed:

1. Place the sea urchins in petri dishes containing seawater.

2. Inject 0.5- 1 mL of 0.5M KCL on each side of the sea urchin's mouth, in order to release gametes from the gonopores, located on the aboral side of the urchin. (You don't have to inject them too deep).

3. If a white fluid is released, it is sperm. Collect the fluid with a pipet, and store it on ice in a plastic tube. Keeping the sperm on ice will slow down metabolic activities and keep the sperm in good condition for the upcoming fertilization process.

4. If an orange fluid is released, it is eggs. Collect the fluid with a pipet, and place it in a 100 mL beaker containing seawater. As soon as the eggs are collected at the bottom of the beaker, dump the seawater, and replace it with fresh seawater.

5. Put 1 drop of the seawater containing eggs on a glass depression slide. You don't have to put a coverslip on it. Now you can take a look at an egg under the microscope. Observe its different parts, such as the cell membrane, cytoplasm, and nucleus.

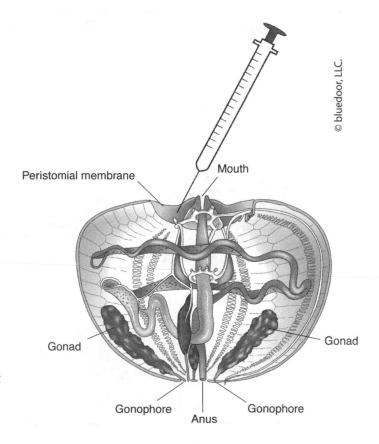

© bluedoor, LLC.

Mouth

Peristomial membrane

Gonad

Gonad

Gonophore

Gonophore

Anus

Draw your observations:

6. Dilute the sperm in seawater by placing 2 drops of the sperm and 10 mL of seawater in a small beaker. Now you are ready to place 1 drop of the sperm solution onto your depression slide containing the eggs.

Note: Add the remaining sperm to leftover eggs in a seawater container so the next class will be able to see early embryos.

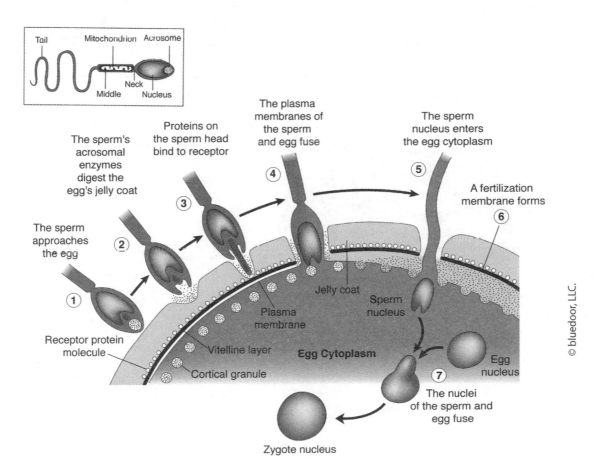

What is the function of the mitochondrion in sperm?

_____

_____

Fertilization Process

The fun part will now begin. Put a coverslip on your slide, and watch the fertilization processes. Observe the rapid movement of sperm that are trying to approach the eggs. Also notice the difference in size and number between the egg and sperm.

Draw your observations.

Why is it important to have species-specific sperm-egg binding?

_____

_____

7. Once fertilization takes place, a physical barrier known as the "fertilization membrane" will be formed.

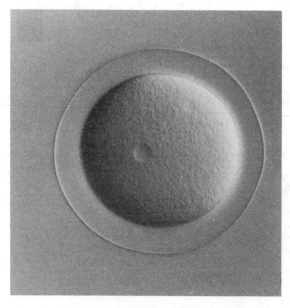

Photograph Courtesy of Dr. Charles A. Ettensohn
Department of Biological Sciences
Carnegie Mellon University

Sea urchin with fertilization membrane

Why is the fertilization membrane necessary?

_____

_____

Embryo Development Embryogenesis

Embryology is the study of different developmental stages prior to becoming an adult. Fertilization allows for the fusion of egg and sperm creating a diploid cell (2N), known as the zygote, prior to the first cell division. Cell division in the early stages of development is known as cleavage. Sea urchins undergo **radial holoblastic cleavage**. This means that prior to the 8-cell embryo stage, the cell divisions will be equal in size and will be positioned next to and on top of each other. After the 8-cell stage, the cells no longer divide in a symmetrical pattern.

Cleavage takes place in stages, starting with the zygote splitting into 2 cells (first cleavage), then into 4 cells (second cleavage), 8, 16, and up to a 128-cell **blastula**. The blastula is the stage of development where the cells have formed a hollow sphere, laying the groundwork for further cell and tissue movement. After the blastula stage, the embryo will enter **gastrulation**. This stage is the process by which cell and tissue movement start to rearrange the blastula to form the different cell layers, which will eventually become internal organs, skeletal structure, and external tissues. We can distinguish the gastrula from the blastula due to an indentation that will start to form on the outside

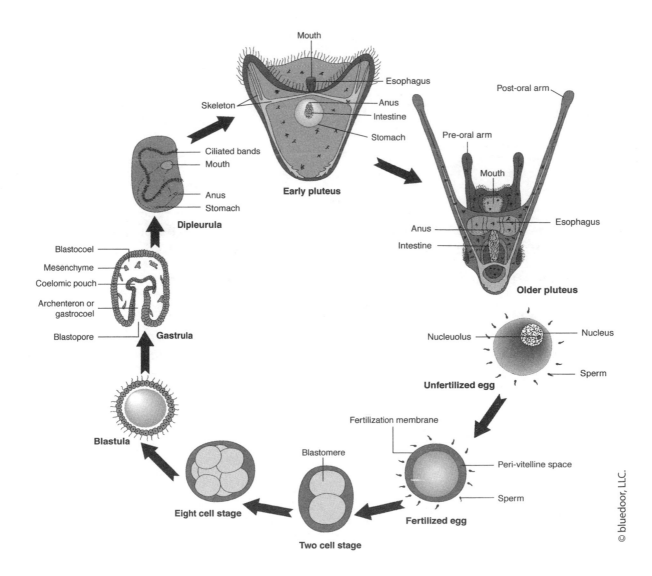

of the sphere. This process of indentation is known as **invagination**, and the area where this takes place is known as the **archenteron** (primitive gut). The gastrula eventually becomes cone shaped, and develops into a larval stage called the **echinopluteus**, also known as "Pluteus Larva" stage.

The newly formed sea urchin stays in its larval stage for up to several months. At the later stage of larval life, a skeleton will start to form, and the echinopluteus will sink to the sea floor. Young urchins are no longer than 1 mL.

Your instructor will provide you with prepared slides of cleavage division.

Observe the first division stages and draw your observations.

Take a clean slide and place 1 drop of the seawater containing the different larval stages (alive ones) that have been formed throughout the different laboratory periods.

Draw and name each of the stages that you are able to see under the microscope.

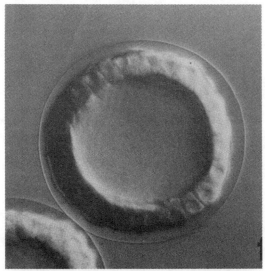

Pre-hatching blastula

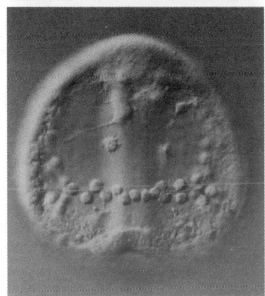

Late gastrula

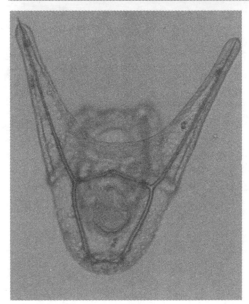

Pluteus larva of the urchin *Lytechinus Variegatus*

Photograph Courtesy of Dr. Charles A. Ettensohn
Department of Biological Sciences
Carnegie Mellon University

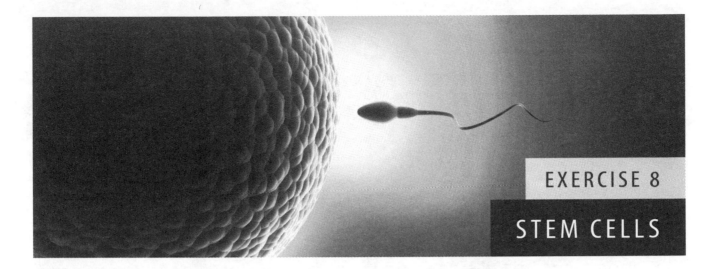

Learning Objectives

The objectives of this chapter are:

- To understand what stem cells are and how they are generated and from where they are isolated ;

- To understand the similarities and differences between various types of stem cells and what makes some types of stem cells more useful in medicine and/or more or less ethically controversial;

- To understand the therapeutic potential of different types of stem cells and the possible risks involved in their use;

- To simulate stem cells in action using planaria regeneration.

INTRODUCTION

The use of stem cells in medicine and research has witnessed periods of great controversy. It is therefore important to have a clear understanding of the pertinent vocabulary, the current state of stem cell technologies, the potential benefits and risks involved in stem cell therapies, and the key differences between different types of stem cells, stem cell sources, and ways to generate or isolate stem cells. Stem cell technologies are rapidly advancing and new information is readily published, so information on this topic ever-changing. This chapter serves as a platform to understand basic concepts in stem cell biology, to provide you with a clear understanding of stem cells and their use in medicine and in research.

Stem cells have the potential to differentiate into either all, many, or a small range of different types of cells depending on the type of stem cell (see following sections).

Differentiation is the process whereby a less specialized cell type changes into a cell type with a more specialized function.

What are Stem Cells?

There are four major types of stem cells currently known that are being investigated by researchers worldwide. These cells differ in their state of differentiation, applicability to modern medicine, research, or ethical properties.

- Embryonic Stem Cells (ESC)

- Adult Stem Cells (ASC)

- Cord-Blood-derived Embryonic-like Stem Cells (CBEs)

- Induced Pluripotent Stem Cells (iPSCs)

Embryonic Stem Cells:

Embryonic stem cells (ESCs) are **pluripotent**. Pluripotency means that these cells can become any/all cell types except for those in tissues that are needed to support the growth of a fetus (e.g. placenta).

ESCs can be kept dividing in culture (carefully in the lab) without differentiating, indefinitely, which allows scientists to grow up many cells of a desired type. As explained prior, differentiation means specialization. We have potentially more than 200 different types of specialized cell types in our bodies that perform various different functions (e.g. epithelial cells, cardiac cells, immune cells, nerve cells, etc.) and these cells then make up our major organs and tissues (e.g. heart, liver, bone, skin, brain, etc.). All of these cell types differ in which genes are expressed at different levels, or simply, what genes are turned on or off within cells. ESCs start off as an essentially blank genetic slate, and as the organism develops from an early embryonic stage, the cells differentiate into groups that become more specialized as differentiation proceeds. Differentiation is coincident with altered levels of gene expression within these cellular populations; these gene expression levels can be used as "markers" by researchers to identify the degree of differentiation.

ESCs are isolated from harvesting the inner cell mass of the **blastocyst**, a structure formed very early on in embryonic development, far before any progressive fetal development has been made. A blastocyst is a hollow ball of about 100 cells that contains a very small cluster of cells inside (this is termed the inner cell mass). The blastocyst develops within the first week after fertilization (the fusion of sperm and egg) has occurred. Although the cells that comprise the inner cell mass of the blastocyst are pluripotent, the blastocyst also contains cells that are **totipotent**, and totipotent cells can make all cell types needed to develop an entire fetus (including the placenta).

ESCs are isolated by dissecting out of the inner cell mass of the blastocyst and grown up on plates containing special media and growth factors that keep the cells in their embryonic state, thus preventing cellular differentiation. Any alteration to either the environmental or growth factor conditions that these cells receive can produce unwarranted cellular differentiation. This can be especially troublesome if you are trying to keep the cells in their pluripotent state! However, planned experiments can actually differentiate ESCs into any cell type by carefully planning the exposed conditions so that a desired cell type can be formed.

Potentially, ESCs can be used for the following applications:

- To study the process of cellular differentiation.

- Treat various medical conditions (e.g. tissue regeneration for burn victims, nerve regeneration, etc.)

- A clinical trial in a dish (**drug screening**). Since ESCs can differentiate into any cell type, we can perform drug screening on the cells to see the negative or positive effects these treatments may have on the cells, in either a simulated disease-state or in normal healthy cells.

- Some research in mice and rats has shown promise for treatment of various nervous system diseases (e.g. Lou Gehrig's disease, multiple sclerosis, Parkinson's disease, spinal cord injury, vision loss etc.)

Since ESCs are derived from the inner-cell mass of a blastocytst, and since the blastocyst in its whole form has the potential to create life, ESCs have been regarded as highly <u>ethically controversial</u>.

In 2001 President George W. Bush signed an executive order that barred the United States Institutes of Health from funding ESC research that used any newly developed ESC lines developed beyond what had existed at or prior to 2001. This left many to suspect that other countries in the world could surpass the United States' level of medical knowledge that could be unlocked by studying ESCs. President Barack H. Obama signed an executive order in 2009 that repealed this policy.

Adult Stem Cells:

Adult stem cells (ASCs) are **multipotent**. Multipotent cells are cells that are not fully, or terminally differentiated and can only differentiate into a limited range of different cell types. ASCs cannot differentiate into any or all cell types as ESCs can. For example, blood multipotent stem cells, termed hematopoietic stem cells, can differentiate into any type of blood cell; these cells are just not known to be capable of making any other cell type *in vivo*, such as the cheek epithelial cells we studied in a previous lab. ASCs found in other organs or tissues such as the retina of the eye are thought to act as repair cells, replacing non-viable cells with new healthy cells.

ASCs cannot be kept dividing in culture indefinitely—these cells have a limited period for which they divide and grow.

ASCs should theoretically be present in virtually any organ or tissue in the body but have only been found in a few organs and tissues at this point in time, although this could be attributed to a lack of defined "multipotent" markers. The ASCs that researchers have found thus far are sparse—being extremely rare or elusive in the body. Potentially the rarity of ASCs is why major damage to vital organs is not readily repaired by ASCs and instead scar tissue forms. ASCs are not only rare, they are also immensely difficult to isolate and isolation usually requires surgical intervention. New research however is uncovering these isolated populations within our many tissues and organs of our bodies.

ASCs can be potentially used to treat diseases, but due to their multipotent characteristics are not as versatile as pluripotent stem cells.

ASCs can be used to screen medically related chemical compounds; however, since these cells are rare, difficult to isolate, and are not as versatile as pluripotent stem cells, use of ASCs in drug screening is not economically feasible. Furthermore, ASCs cannot be used to study the beginning stages of human or other organism development and what effects different compounds might have during this critical time of development directly. However, drug screenings on these cellular populations may provide large insight into how the body repairs itself, and potentially, how to enhance the repair process.

Today, ASCs are routinely being used to treat blood cancer leukemia. Leukemia and other blood disorders can be treated with adult bone marrow and/or adult peripheral blood stem cells. The diseased blood cells are destroyed and the patient's bone marrow or peripheral blood is replaced with stem cells from the bone marrow or peripheral blood of a suitable donor.

Since ASCs derive from adult tissue, and do not have the potential to create life, ASCs are not considered ethically controversial.

CORD BLOOD-DERIVED EMBRYONIC-LIKE STEM CELLS

Cord Blood-derived embryonic-like stem cells (CBEs) are historically known for being able to differentiate into any type of blood cell, having primarily multipotent activity. However, recent research within the past few years has demonstrated that CBEs have pluripotent-like abilities in vitro (in the lab, in a predefined setting). However, some scientists still believe that there is no difference between CBEs and multipotent adult hematopoetic stem cells in vivo. Nevertheless, given the research to suggest that pluripotent cells can be isolated from CBE populations in vitro, CBEs could have far ranging uses in therapeutic medicine.

CBEs cannot be kept dividing in culture indefinitely, but can be stored. Many research groups are focusing on ways to better expand and maintain CBEs in in vitro culture systems.

CBEs are not ethically controversial, as they are isolated from the umbilical cord after birth.

Commonly, CBEs are used to treat blood and immune system disorders such as leukemia (a blood cell cancer), anemia (a decrease in the number of red blood cell in the body), and autoimmune diseases (diseases where the immune system targets actually healthy tissue or cellular components).

Similar limitations apply to CBEs as ASCs in their use for drug screening applications; however, with recent evidence suggesting that CBEs do have pluripotent capabilities, CBEs could be a very useful alternative to ESCs in these studies.

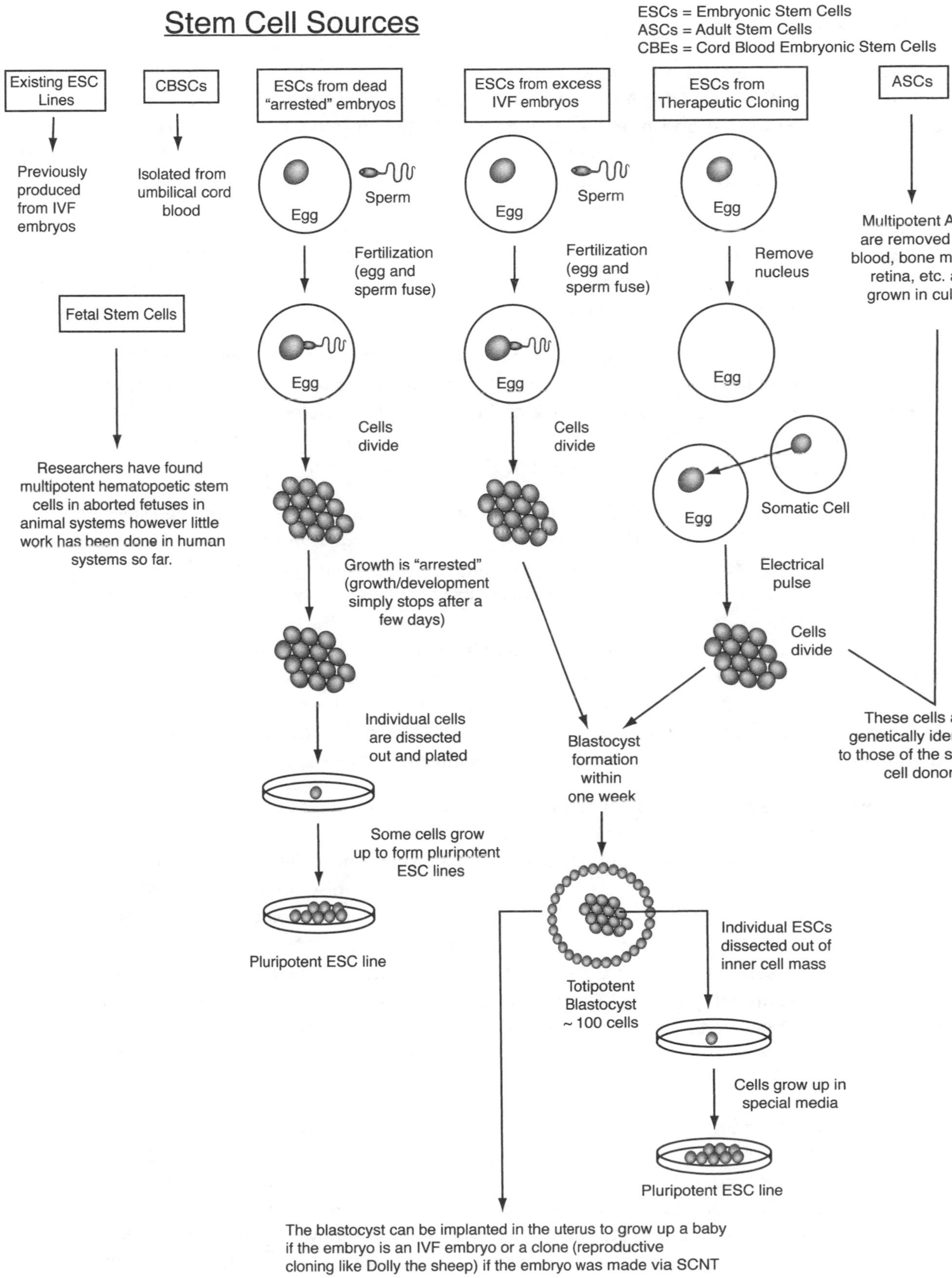

Stem Cell Sources

ESCs = Embryonic Stem Cells
ASCs = Adult Stem Cells
CBEs = Cord Blood Embryonic Stem Cells

Existing ESC Lines

Previously produced from IVF embryos

CBSCs

Isolated from umbilical cord blood

Fetal Stem Cells

Researchers have found multipotent hematopoetic stem cells in aborted fetuses in animal systems however little work has been done in human systems so far.

ESCs from dead "arrested" embryos

Egg   Sperm

Fertilization (egg and sperm fuse)

Egg

Cells divide

Growth is "arrested" (growth/development simply stops after a few days)

Individual cells are dissected out and plated

Some cells grow up to form pluripotent ESC lines

Pluripotent ESC line

ESCs from excess IVF embryos

Egg   Sperm

Fertilization (egg and sperm fuse)

Egg

Cells divide

ESCs from Therapeutic Cloning

Egg

Remove nucleus

Egg

Egg   Somatic Cell

Electrical pulse

Cells divide

ASCs

Multipotent ASCs are removed from blood, bone marrow, retina, etc. and grown in culture

These cells are genetically identical to those of the somatic cell donor

Blastocyst formation within one week

Totipotent Blastocyst ~ 100 cells

Individual ESCs dissected out of inner cell mass

Cells grow up in special media

Pluripotent ESC line

The blastocyst can be implanted in the uterus to grow up a baby if the embryo is an IVF embryo or a clone (reproductive cloning like Dolly the sheep) if the embryo was made via SCNT

Figure1: Stem cell sources.

©bluedoor, LLC

Stem Cell Sources

Stem cells can be obtained from several sources. There are some already existing embryonic stem cell lines (ESCs) that are available for research uses. ESCs can also be produced via therapeutic cloning, and also from live and, more recently, dead (growth "arrested") In Vitro Fertilization embryos (IVF embryos). As stated previously, adult stem cells have been found in some organs and can be isolated in small quantities however usually via very invasive methods.

In **therapeutic cloning**, the nucleus of an egg is removed and replaced with the nucleus of a **somatic cell** (all body cells, except for the sex/germ cells (egg/sperm) are referred to as somatic cells). This technology is called **Somatic Cell Nuclear Transfer** (**SCNT**). The new cell that is produced is then induced to divide by exposing it to an electrical pulse.

The new cells divide until the blastocyst is formed and the inner cell mass is then dissected to separate out individual cells which are grown up to form new embryonic stem cell lines. These new ESCs are genetically identical to the cells of the person who donated the original somatic cell so these cells can be used to treat diseases and tissue/organ damage within the donor with little chance of rejection. This is an important benefit of using this method.

ESCs can also be obtained via **In Vitro Fertilization** (**IVF**) technology. In IVF, an egg and sperm are allowed to fuse outside of the body and then the now fertilized egg is implanted in the woman's uterus to grow into a baby—this is done to help couples who have trouble conceiving for different reasons. Often times, there will be several embryos left over that the couple no longer needs once they have successfully become pregnant. These extra embryos are thrown away when the couple no longer needs them. Instead of just disposing of them, they could be allowed to develop for a few days and then used to obtain ESCs from the inner cell mass of the blastocyst (the same way as is done with therapeutic cloning). These ESCs would not be genetically identical to any one person but ESCs are less likely to be rejected than adult stem cells when used to treat diseases because of their undifferentiated state. Adult stem cells are already somewhat differentiated.

Just recently (September 2006), an article was released regarding stem cells being obtained from dead, "arrested" embryos for the first time. The term "arrested" here is referring to their growth/development. It is essentially saying that the growth/development of these cells has stopped. These "arrested" embryos were produced via IVF technology. The egg and sperm were allowed to fuse and the new cells then began dividing but the embryos stopped developing after a few days. The researchers watched these arrested cells for 24 hours to be sure that the embryos did not develop any further (to be sure that they were "dead") before separating the cells and putting them in special media containing growth factors and factors that prevent differentiation. Out of all of the cells that they plated, one grew up to form a new ESC line even though the embryo had "died". The idea here is the same as when we use organs for transplants from people who have died—some of the cells in the embryo were still functional.

This might sound like the solution to the stem cell debate but there are still some concerns with this new method. For example, there may be people who will not agree that this group's definition of a dead embryo is acceptable. The origin of these cells is also a problem from the researcher's perspective. These are cells that came from embryos that were abnormal; if the embryos had been normal then they would not have stopped developing. We don't know why the embryos did not develop correctly and it may be due to some genetic defect. If that is the case then these cells may not end up being useful for research or treatment.

Adult Stem Cells (ASCs) can be removed from the blood, bone marrow, retinas, and some other organs in which they have been identified and grown in culture. The major benefit of using adult stem cells is the lack of controversy regarding the potential life of an embryo since we are not using embryos here. The major problems with ASCs are: a) they are sparse, b) we haven't found them in many different organs, c) they are difficult to isolate, d) they can only be used to grow up some specific cell types and e) they cannot be maintained indefinitely in the lab which makes it difficult to obtain enough cells to use for in therapy.

As stated previously, Cord Blood-derived Stem Cells (CBSCs) are obtained from the umbilical cord blood of newborns. Use of these cells is less controversial than the use of embryonic stem cells however the current research indicates that CBSCs are not very different or significantly more useful than ASCs.

Our last source, which is probably one of the most controversial, is the fetus. Research in animal systems has shown that stem cells can be found in aborted fetuses. There has not been much research in human systems at this point in time but blood stem cells have been found in aborted mouse fetuses. Further studies in animals will be required to determine whether or not there are any more useful cells in these aborted fetuses but the current research suggests that these stem cells are not very different or more useful than ASCs or CBSCs which are less controversial.

Potential Concerns

For as much potential good that stem cell therapy may one day do, there are many concerns for scientists that highlight the need for more intensive research into these cells.

Embryonic stem cells are able to divide indefinitely in the lab. Because of this, we have to think about how being kept in an environment that is not normal for them over an extended period of time might affect them. The ESCs are receiving different signals and growth factors in the lab than they would in our bodies and we can't be sure what this might do to them without further research. We also have to consider the fact that cancer cells can also divide indefinitely. We will need to more clearly define the line between stem cells and cancer cells before we can use them for therapy. We also still have much to do in terms of determining the best way to push these cells to develop into the specific cell types that we want to produce.

Please fill in the following table from your reading.

Table 1: Comparison of Stem Cell Types.

Stem cell type	Potency	Source	Potential Uses	Controversy?
Embryonic Stem Cells (ESCs)				
Adult Stem Cells (ASCs)				
Cord-blood derived embryonic-like stem cells (CBEs)				
Induced Pluripotent Stem Cells (iPSCs) – *see below!*				

INDUCED PLURIPOTENT STEM CELLS

What if we were to say you could generate a pluripotent stem cell without having to isolate the cell from a blastocyst, as is the case with ESCs? Is this science fiction or reality? But wait, what about the ethical debate?

Induced pluripotent stem cells (iPSCs) represent a novel strategy to stem cell generation. iPSCs are derived from adult cells that have been genetically altered by manipulating gene expression or environmental conditions to revert/reprogram/un-differentiate the adult somatic cell back into a pluripotent cell. iPSCs, as the name suggests, are pluripotent stem cells that are capable of differentiating into any cell type just as an ESC would be capable of. In fact, a somatic cell can be reprogrammed back to pluripotency with as few as 4 select genes inserted through a variety of different methods, including viral-mediated gene transfer and synthetic mRNA expression, amongst a variety of methods.

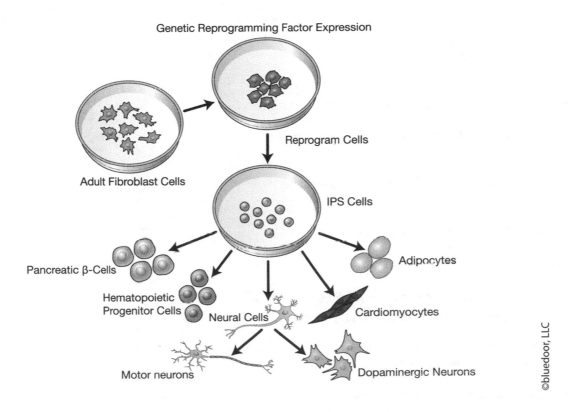

Figure 2: iPSC generation from somatic cell.

iPSCs are not considered ethically controversial because no blastocyst is created in order to generate iPSCs, thus no "potential for life" occurs during the isolation/generation/reprogramming process. Theoretically, you can become the personal donor of your own pluripotent stem cell line, bypassing ethical and potential immunological complications that are associated with the use of ESCs in transplant studies, since the reprogrammed cells derive initially from you, and contain the same genome, your genome.

iPSCs are excellent candidate cells for drug screening as, in theory, scientists can specifically test how a given drug will interact with a patient's cells' genome specifically. Since we are not all the same and everyone has a slightly different genome due to the nature of genetic diversity, this feature of iPSCs allows for the potential for patient-specific drug therapies in the future.

However, since iPSCs derive from adult somatic cells, these cells have the possibility to have accumulated mutations or other cellular defects that could impair their use as an embryonic stem cell alternative. Future research will help to delineate the differences between ESCs and iPSCs and expand the usefulness of iPSCs.

In 2012, the two people who led much of the exploration and research involving iPSCs received the Nobel Prize in Physiology and Medicine.

Research is gaining popularity on iPSCs, and scientists are scrambling to fulfill the promise that iPSCs can be used to revolutionize modern medicine. The future of iPSC efficacy as a therapeutic vector has shown some early success, as researchers have already developed functional organs and complex tissues using this technology in mice. Human clinical trials that use iPSCs are just on the horizon.

REFERENCES

University of Utah
http://learn.genetics.utah.edu/units/stemcells

National Institutes of Health
http://stemcells.nih.gov

International Society for Stem Cell Research
http://www.isscr.org

Stem Cells Cultivated from Dead Embryo
By Rick Weiss
The Washington Post (Sept. 2006)

Engage—Stem Cells Information Booklet
Northwest Association for Biomedical Research www.nwabr.org

Robinton D.A., Daley G.Q., 2012. The promise of induced pluripotent stem cells in research and therapy. Nature. 481: 295-305.

http://www.eurostemcell.org/films

PLANARIA – A MODEL SPECIES FOR EXPERIMENTAL REGENERATION

Planarian flatworms contain a remarkable adult stem cell system that is amicable to the study of cellular differentiation and regeneration.

In fact, one planarian can be "cut" into many planarians, where the missing parts from the initial planarian are also simultaneously re-grown. The cutting breaks cellular matrix attachment points and kick starts cellular repair and differentiation. For instance, if the head of a planarian is cut off, both the head and tail sections will regenerate to form two planarians. This is the same mechanism the planarian use to asexually reproduce, as a planarian will literally split itself in half to reproduce; this is termed "fragmentation". Planarian also "self-renew" their entire cellular population every so-often, and are known to shrink and enlarge in size, depending upon local nutrient abundance!

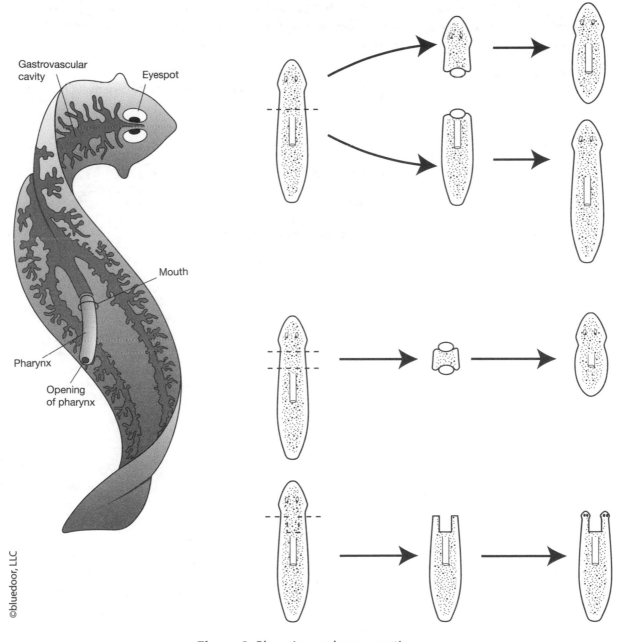

Figure 3: Planarian and regeneration.

So how do planaria do this?

Planaria contain adult somatic cells known as neoblasts that are pluripotent, and capable of differentiating into any cell type of the planarian body plan. These are found throughout the planaria's body.

In lab this week, your lab instructor will guide you through an experiment to see if you can too regenerate planaria in the lab by simply "cutting" the planarian.

Instructions for Planarian Regeneration Experiment

1. Obtain a few planaria from your lab instructor and place into petri dishes containing spring water supplemented with a few drops of the water the planarian came with.

2. Using a razor blade or a scalpel, make cuts into the planarian as discussed prior simply by cutting the head of the planarian off and leaving the tail. You can experiment with the cuts based upon the number of planaria your group has been allocated.

3. Label your petri dishes with the cuts you made and your group's and TA's name. Next week in class you can check on the status of your planarian and see if experimental regeneration took place.

References

Rink J.C.,2013. Stem cell systems and regeneration in planaria. Dev Genes Evol. 223:67-84.

https://wiki.umn.edu/pub/Biol4361/LabMaterials/13_Planarian_Regeneration.pdf

Check the articles above for great figures and illustrations on planaria!

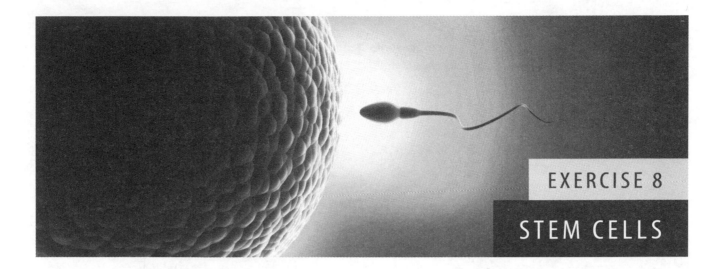

POST-LAB QUESTIONS

Please compare and contrast the different types of stem cells discussed below, paying close attention to comparing versatility (differentiation potential), efficacy in medicine, and ethical dilemmas.

1. What are the four major stem cell sources currently being investigated?

   Embryonic
   Tissue specific
   Mesenchymal
   Induced pluripotent

2. What is the difference between cells that are multipotent, cells that are totipotent and cells that are pluripotent?

   Totipotent – can turn into anything
   pluripotent – anything except placenta
   Multipotent – can develop into limited number of all types

3. Embryonic Stem Cells generated via therapeutic cloning are genetically identical to the cells of the person who donated the original somatic cell used for SCNT. Why is this important?

   So they won't rejected

4. What is one advantage of using embryonic stem cells instead of adult stem cells? What is one advantage of using adult stem cells instead of embryonic stem cells?

— embryonic can be used for anything

— adult can formed at ready

5. What are two reasons why the use of dead, "arrested" embryos might not be a very good alternative stem cell source?

potential for life or death

6. There is much that we still need to learn about stem cells before we can begin to safely use them in a wider range of therapies. What similarity do stem cells share with cancer cells that requires further investigation?

keep growing

7. How are planaria capable of regeneration?

cells are like stem cells

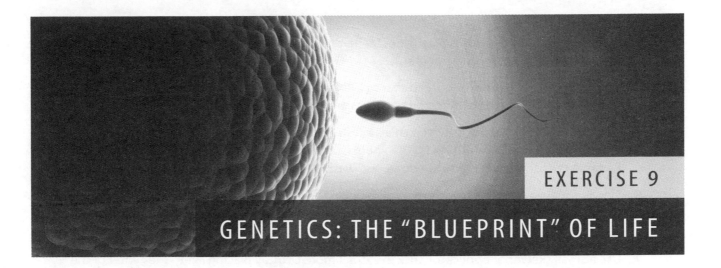

GENETICS: THE "BLUEPRINT" OF LIFE

Objectives

The objectives of this exercise are to understand DNA and the genetics behind heredity.

INTRODUCTION

In 1953, Watson and Crick first proposed the double helix model of DNA. Further research elucidated the exact nature of the helix as composed of pairings of purine and pyrimidine nitrogenous bases. This relatively simple molecule is the basis for **heredity**, the passing on of characteristics from parents to their children. **Genetics** is the study of the process in which characteristics are passed along through the generations.

Experiment 1: DNA Extraction

Before we go into how traits are passed on from parent to offspring, it is important to realize that DNA is found in ALL biological organisms. To observe DNA, we will be extracting it from strawberries.

PROCEDURE

1. Begin by making the DNA extraction solution. First, make an 8% soap/water solution by combining 10 mL of distilled water with 0.8 mL of NON-ANTIBACTERIAL dishwashing detergent in a beaker (if you are using a pipette, 0.8 mL is about 26 drops).

2. Then make a 2% saltwater solution by combining 10 mL of distilled water with 0.2 g of salt. Mix thoroughly, and pour this solution into the beaker containing your soap/water solution. Mix the two together. This is your DNA extraction solution.

3. Place 2 or 3 strawberries in a plastic freezer bag, remove all the air from the bag, and seal it. Then thoroughly crush the strawberries.

4. Add 10 mL of the DNA extraction buffer to the freezer bag. Again, remove all the air, seal it, and thoroughly mix the mashed strawberries and buffer together.

5. Pour some of the mixture onto the cheesecloth, and carefully strain the mixture into a test tube using a funnel. Be sure that ONLY liquid is strained into the tube. Fill 1/4 of the test tube. Remove the funnel when you are done, and wash out the cheesecloth.

6. Slowly squeeze 10 mL of isopropyl alcohol down the inside of the test tube. Do this gently, as the alcohol should form a layer on top of the strawberry mixture. A stringy layer should begin to form. This is the extracted DNA.

7. Use a small skewer or applicator stick to extract more DNA by placing it into the center of the test tube and gently rotating. DO NOT STIR. This causes the DNA to spool onto the skewer.

Why is the DNA attracted to the layer of alcohol?

its not soluble

Genetics & Heredity

Before we go into the discussion, lets see how much you know about genetics and heredity.

GENETICS QUIZ: Answer True or False to the following:

1. _____ Identical twins are more closely related than fraternal twins.

2. _____ Fraternal twins are more closely related than they are to other siblings.

3. _____ A child receives half of his/her genes from the father and half of his/her genes from the mother.

4. _____ Children born to older parents are not as lively as those children born to younger parents.

5. _____ All of a father's traits are expressed in his child.

6. _____ Males are biologically stronger than females.

7. _____ More males are born annually than females.

8. _____ The fetus is affected by the mother's emotional state during her pregnancy.

9. _____ The emotional state of the fetus is affected by the attitudes of the parents towards each other.

10. _____ Unusual food cravings are the cause of birthmarks.

11. _____ If an individual loses a limb in an accident, then the child will be born without that limb.

12. _____ Many inherited traits do not appear.

13. _____ Color-blindness is more prevalent in males than in females.

14. _____ If your parents are math whizzes, then you will be a math whiz, too.

15. _____ The stars, moon, or planets determine the temperament of the child.

16. _____ Red hair is caused by a virus.

17. _____ If you want to have a baby girl, conceive the child during a full moon.

18. _____ Two healthy people can have a child with a genetic disease.

19. _____ The sex of the child is determined by the mother.

As you can see from the quiz, there are some traits that are passed from parent to child (i.e., eye color) and some that aren't. There are also some traits that are present in the offspring, but may not be visible in the parent (i.e. cystic fibrosis). Regardless of the trait that's inherited, it's all packaged in the same way – as coded information in the form of hereditary units known as **genes**. These genes are found on specific positions on a **chromosome**.

The basic form of DNA is a double helix. Simply put, this is a ladder that is twisted around on itself. The rungs of the ladder are composed of groupings of **purines** and **pyrimidines**, two different types of nitrogenous bases. The sides of this ladder are composed of alternating phosphorous and deoxyribose sugar molecules (**Figure 1**).

All of this is found within a structure known as the **chromosome**. If you imagine the chromosome as an apartment building, then each apartment is equivalent to a **gene** – or the hereditary unit. And the DNA – the coded information – is the tenant in each of these apartments.

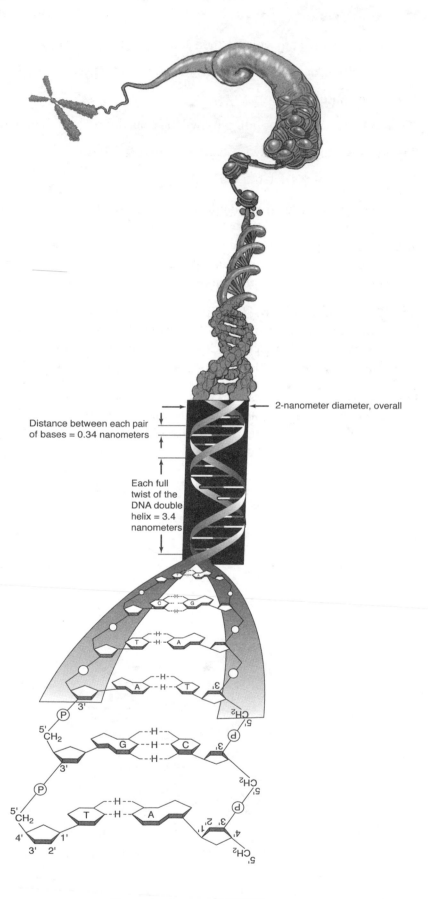

Figure 1: Structure of DNA.

It is also possible to have different molecular forms of a gene. These are known as **alleles**. Alleles are located at the same position on homologous chromosomes, and are separated from each other during meiosis (If we go back to the apartment analogy, homologous chromosomes would be two identical buildings on the same block. The alleles would be the differences between apartments 2B of both buildings.). A child receives two alleles for every trait, one from the mother and one from the father. Within every individual, each and every cell has the same number of chromosomes, and generally come in pairs (except for sex cells). Humans, for instance, have 23 pairs, or 46 chromosomes. However, each set of chromosomes carries different alleles, since each set comes from a different parent. Regarding a particular trait (like hair color), if the chromosomes you receive from both parents have the same allele (in other words, code for the same characteristic – like brown hair), you are said to be homozygous for that allele. If both alleles are dominant, you are said to be **homozygous dominant**. **Dominant traits** occur more frequently in a population, and are usually represented by capital letters (brown hair is more frequent than blond hair). Therefore, if you had the alleles **BB** for hair color, you would be homozygous dominant and have brown hair.

If both alleles are **recessive**, you are said to be **homozygous recessive**. **Recessive traits** occur less frequently in a population, and are usually represented by lower case letters (blond hair is less frequent than brown hair). Therefore, if you had the alleles **bb** for hair color, you would be homozygous recessive and have blond hair.

If you have both the dominant and the recessive forms of the allele, you are said to be **heterozygous** for that trait. In most cases, the heterozygous form expresses the characteristic of the dominant allele. Therefore, if you the alleles **Bb** for hair color, you would be heterozygous and have brown hair.

BB = homozygous dominant =

bb = homozygous recessive =

Bb = heterozygous =

The **genotype** of an organism expresses the particular alleles of an organism instead of its physical appearance. Organisms with the same physical appearance may have different genotypes. For example, a person may have brown hair, but their genotype could be either **BB** or **Bb**. The **phenotype** of an organism expresses its physical appearance instead of its actual genetic makeup. For example, you would say the phenotype of a person is "brown hair." *Genotypes always predict the phenotype, but phenotypes cannot always reveal the genotype!*

PROCEDURE

We can predict which traits will be hereditarily passed on to the offspring of two parents using a **Punnett Square**. This is a mathematical device used by geneticists to show the ratios of alleles and traits that may be passed on.

Part A: Single-Trait Inheritance

To examine the ratios of one characteristic (for example, hair color), a **monohybrid cross** is carried out. Let's say one parent has red hair and the other has brown hair. First, determine the genotypes and phenotypes of the parents.

Hair color will be represented by the letter "R", with brown hair (R) being dominant and red hair (r) being recessive.

If the father is homozygous recessive (red head), then his genotype is **rr.**

If the mother is heterozygous (brown hair), then her genotype is **Rr.**

Next, construct a Punnett Square and place the genotypes on top and on the side.

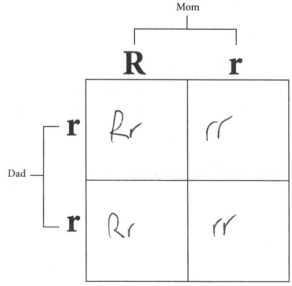

Finally, carry out the cross by combining the specific alleles in the specific blocks:

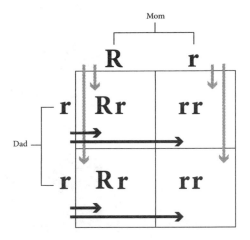

You are left with 2 children with the genotype Rr (50%) and 2 children with the genotype rr (50%). The phenotypes are 50% brown and 50% red.

Further Examples

Here are some more examples of completely dominant traits that are easily observed.

Mid Digital Hair: The presence of hair on the finger between the hand and first knuckle indicates the dominant condition (HH or Hh). Complete absence of hair indicates the recessive condition (hh). Even the slightest bit of hair indicates the dominant condition.

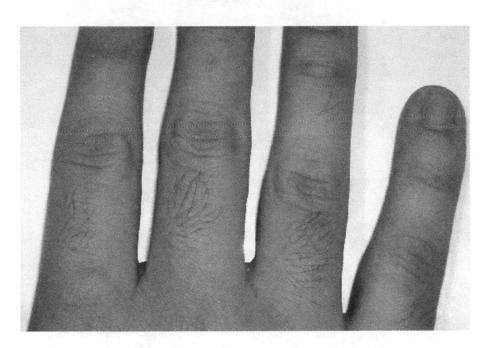

Tongue Rolling: The ability to roll one's tongue indicates the dominant condition (TT or Tt). The homozygous recessive condition (tt) results in an inability to roll one's tongue.

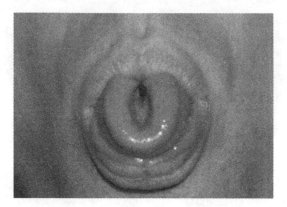

Widow's Peak: This is a distinct downward point in the hairline along one's forehead. This is the dominant condition. The recessive condition results in a continuous hairline.

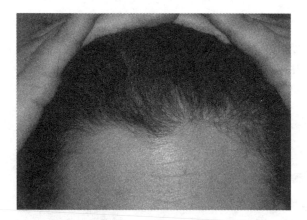

Dominant condition

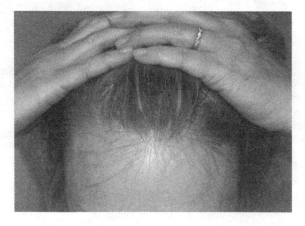

Recessive condition

Earlobe Attachment: The dominant condition results in detached earlobes (EE or Ee). The recessive condition (ee) results in earlobes attached directly to the head.

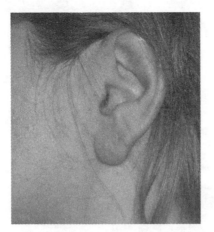

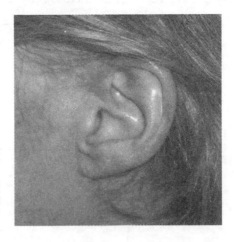

Detached (dominant condition)   **Attached (recessive condition)**

Hitchhiker's Thumb: The dominant condition results in individuals who cannot bend their thumbs backwards to 45°. Homozygous recessive individuals (hh) can bend their thumbs at least 45°, if not farther.

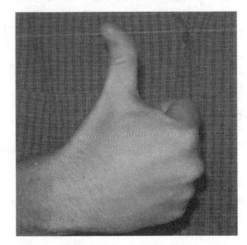

Dominant Condition   **Recessive Condition**

Applied Problem: Your mother has blue eyes and is homozygous recessive. Your father has brown eyes and is heterozygous. Carry out a monohybrid cross to determine the possible combination of genotypes and phenotypes for their crossing.

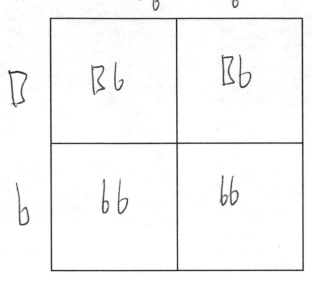

What are the possible genotypes and phenotypes for the offspring of these parents?

their child can be homozygous

recessive or heterozygous

Part B: Two-Trait Inheritance

Now let's analyze two sets of genes at the same time. This is done through a **dihybrid cross**, where two characteristics (i.e., eye color and height) will be examined. Let's carry out a cross between a father who has brown eyes and is tall, with a mother who has blue eyes and is short. Again, start by selecting the genotypes and phenotypes of the parents.

Eye color will be represented by the letter "B", with brown eyes (B) dominant over blue eyes (b). Height will be represented by the letter "T", with tall (T) being dominant over short (t).

If the father is heterozygous for eye color and homozygous dominant for height, then his genotype is **BbTT**.

If the mother is homozygous recessive for eye color and is homozygous recessive for height, then her genotype is **bbtt**.

Next, determine the four possible allelic combinations from the father and mother using the FOIL method (First Outer Inner Last).

Father: **BbTT**

1. First: BbTt = BT
2. Outer : BbTT = BT
3. Inner: BbTT = bT
4. Last: BbTT = bT

Mother: **bbtt**

1. First: **bb**tt = bt
2. Outer: **bb**tt = bt
3. Inner: **bb**tt = bt
4. Last: **bb**tt = bt

	BT	BT	bT	bT
bt				
bt				
bt				
bt				

Now carry out the cross by combining specific alleles down and across to determine the possible frequency of traits.

	BT	BT	bT	bT
bt	BbTt	BbTt	bbTt	bbTt
bt	BbTt	BbTt	bbTt	bbTt
bt	BbTt	BbTt	bbTt	bbTt
bt	BbTt	BbTt	bbTt	bbTt

Applied Problem: Brown eyes are dominant over blue, and curly hair is dominant over straight. Your father is heterozygous for brown eyes and has straight hair. Your mother is recessive for blue eyes and is heterozygous with curly hair. Conduct a dihybrid cross to determine the possible allelic combinations of genotypes and phenotypes for their crossing.

	Bh	Bh	bh	bh
bH	BbHh	BbHh	bbHh	bbHh
bh	Bbhh	Bbhh	bbhh	bbhh
bH	BbHh	BbHh	bbHh	bbHh
bh	Bbhh	Bbhh	bbhh	bbhh

D - Bb bb

M - bb Hh

Part C: Sex-Linked Traits

Sometimes the inheritance of traits is linked to the last pair of chromosomes. These are called **sex chromosomes,** and they determine the sex of an individual (XX = female, and XY = male). Several genetic disorders are passed along on these chromosomes. One such disorder is hemophilia. Hemophilia prevents the blood from clotting and will be given the allele h. The normal blood clotting allele is H.

So the genotype and phenotype of the parents are as follows:

Father: $X_H Y_O$ (Non-carrier of hemophilia, and the Y chromosome does not carrier this gene).

Mother: $X_H X_h$ (Doesn't have hemophilia, but is a carrier).

Next, construct your Punnett Square.

	X_H	Y_O
X_H		
X_h		

Now, carry out the sex-linked cross.

	X_H	Y_O
X_H	$X_H X_H$	$X_H Y_O$
X_h	$X_H X_h$	$X_h Y_O$

What are the chances of this couple having a child with hemophilia? What is the sex of this child?

~~XY~~. 25%. ~~female~~ Male

Applied Problem: You mother (XX) carries the gene for Parkinson's disease (d), a sex-linked trait, but she does not have the disease. Your father (XY) was just diagnosed with the disease last year. What are the possible outcomes for your future brothers and sisters?

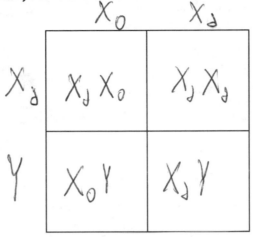

Other common sex linked traits are color blindness, congenital night blindness, and muscular dystrophy.

Part D: Other Types of Dominance

Not all dominant and recessive alleles are expressed this simply. There are exceptions. One example is **incomplete dominance**. This is basically just a blending of traits, where the heterozygous form is a blend of the homozygous dominant and homozygous recessive. A good example is when a red flower (RR) is crossed with a white flower (R'R'). The succeeding generation contains all pink flowers (RR') because neither R nor R' is truly dominant over the other allele.

| (RR) | + | (R'R') | = | (RR') |

Another example is **co-dominance**, where there is no real dominant or recessive allele. Instead, both alleles are fully expressed in the heterozygous form. A good example of co-dominance is a person's blood type. The AB blood type expresses the characteristics of both blood types A and B. Therefore, the alleles for blood type must be co-dominant.

Applications of DNA Testing and Genetics

Forensics

Any type of organism can be identified by examination of DNA sequences unique to that species. To identify individuals, forensic scientists scan 13 DNA regions that vary from person to person, and use the data to create a DNA profile of that individual (sometimes called a **DNA fingerprint**). There is an extremely small chance that another person has the same DNA profile for a particular set of regions.

This is an example of forensic DNA multilocus fingerprinting to match trace evidence from a crime with suspects.

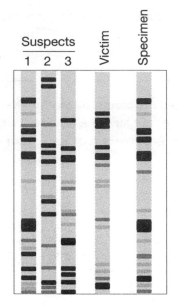

Which suspect matches the specimen?

Suspect 1

DNA fingerprinting has led to the improved efficiency of our judicial system. By matching DNA profiles with evidence, authorities can link a suspect to a crime or crime scene. The FBI has an online database of more than a million profiles that they compare to crime scene samples; more than 500 positive matches come up a week. In contrast, at least 10 innocent people have been freed from death row in the United States after DNA evidence from their cases was studied. About 30% of DNA profile comparisons done by the FBI result in excluding someone as a suspect.

Paternity Testing

In cases of uncertain paternity, it is possible to compare the paternal fragments in the child's DNA with those from the alleged father. When the DNA fragments fail to match, the alleged father is excluded as the biological father. A failed match is absolute, because the alleged father could not have contributed the child's paternal fragment.

The following is an example of multilocus fingerprinting to establish parentage. Examine the bands detected in DNA from the child that are not detected with the DNA from the mother.

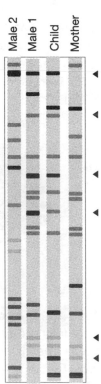

Which male is the biological father of the child?

Male 1

Other uses of DNA and genetic technologies include transgenic crops (heartier tomatoes that will survive during shipping), cloning (Dolly the sheep), gene therapies in the treatment of disease, (AIDS research), stem cell research, and health assessments (to screen for disease).

Practice Problems:

UNLESS OTHERWISE STATED, ASSUME A TRAIT IS COMPLETELY DOMINANT

1. People who are double jointed possess the dominant (J). Normal joints are represented by the recessive condition (jj). Please complete a cross between a couple both of whom possess the heterozygous condition. What percentage of their offspring will have normal joints? What percentage will be double jointed?

2. Dimples represent the dominant condition (D), whereas the lack of dimples represents the recessive condition (d). Please complete a cross between Peter, who has no dimples, and his wife Sally, who is heterozygous for dimples.

3. The color pattern known as piebald in ball pythons is controlled by a simple recessive trait. If two ball pythons with the regular color pattern were bred, what percentage of their offspring would be piebald? What is the genotypic ratio? What is the phenotypic ratio?

4. Colorblindness is a sex-linked trait. The gene is found on the X chromosome. There-fore, a male who is XBYO, or a female who is XBXB or XBXb will have normal vision. A male who is XbYO, or a female who is XbXb, will be colorblind. Brown eyes are also completely dominant over blue eyes. Perform a dihybrid cross between Paul, who is homozygous dominant for brown eyes and is color blind, with Annie, who has blue eyes and carries the gene for colorblindness, but is not colorblind.

5. Phenylketonuria (PKU) is a disease that prevents people from digesting phenylalanine, a substance found in almost all food items. Those with a mutated gene are unable to produce the necessary enzymes to digest phenylalanine. If left untreated, the build up of phenyalanine can cause brain damage and mental retardation. Perform a cross between Henry, who is homozygous dominant and does not have the illness, and his wife Diana who does.

6. Snapdragons exhibit incomplete dominance in that the crossing of red flowers (RR) with white flowers (R'R') produces pink flowers (RR'). What happens when you cross the offspring of a red and white flower? What are the possible genotypes and phenotypes?

7. Human blood type is a good example of co-dominance. There are three possible alleles for blood type: IA, IB, and IO. Since we inherit one set of genes from mom and one from dad, it is the combination of these alleles that determine our blood type. By using the chart given below, perform a cross be-tween an individual with type AB blood with someone with type O blood.

GENOTYPE	PHENOTYPE
$I^A I^A$	Type A
$I^A I^O$	Type A
$I^B I^B$	Type B
$I^B I^O$	Type B
$I^A I^B$	Type AB
$I^O I^O$	Type O

What are the possible blood types of their offspring?

8. Tongue rolling (T) and possession of a widow's peak hairline (W) are both dominant traits. Complete a cross between Nathan, who is heterozygous for tongue rolling and homozygous dominant with a widow's peak, and his wife Samantha, who cannot roll her tongue and is heterozygous with a widow's peak. What percentage of their children will have widow's peaks and be able to roll their tongues? What percentage of their children will have widow's peaks an be unable to roll their tongues?

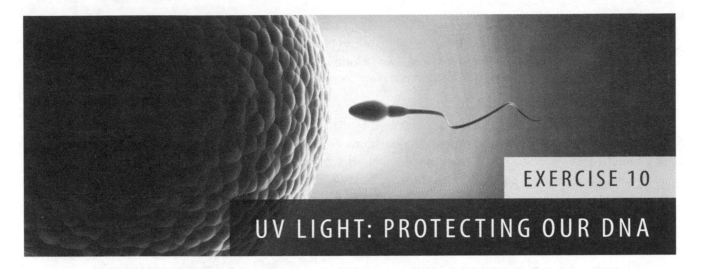

UV LIGHT: PROTECTING OUR DNA

Objectives

The objectives of this exercise are to understand the harmful effects of ultraviolet (UV) radiation; to understand the Sun Protection Factor (SPF) rating system of sunscreens; to experimentally determine the effectiveness of sunscreens, sunglasses, and other materials to absorb UV radiation; and to experimentally use yeast cells to demonstrate the lethal effects of UV radiation.

INTRODUCTION

Light moves in waves that resemble the waves that we see in the ocean. These waves carry energy from one location to another. The waves have what we call a crest and a trough. The crest is the highest point of the wave, and trough is the lowest point. When we talk about wavelengths, we are talking about the length of one full cycle of a wave, which means that we can measure it in a couple of different ways. We can measure the distance between two adjacent crests, between two adjacent troughs, or between any two equal points in the wave cycle.

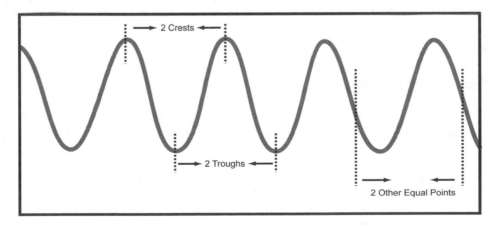

© bluedoor, LLC.

When we talk about wavelengths of light, we talk about them in terms of nanometers (nm). One meter is equal to just over 3 feet. The prefix nano means 10-9, so we are talking about very small numbers here. If we say that we are looking at light with a wavelength of 480 nm, this means that it is 0.00000048 meters. This is very much shorter than an inch.

When we talk about light, we have different kinds of light, and the kind of light that we have depends on how long the wavelength is. All the different colors that we can see are part of the visible light spectrum, and each color has its own wavelength.

The sun radiates energy over a wide spectrum of wavelengths, half of which are in the form of visible light. The other "invisible" half includes **ultraviolet** (**UV**) **radiation**, whose shorter wavelengths carry more energetic radiation and more potential harm. Even though the Earth's ozone layer serves as a protective shield, not all UV radiation is eliminated. UV radiation at different wavelengths delivers varying effects, and is classified into three types: **UVA**, **UVB**, **UVC**.

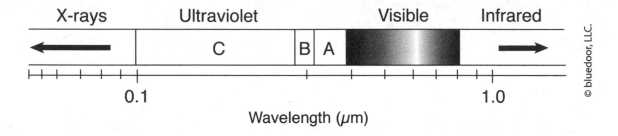

UVA (320-400 nm): These are the longest UV wavelengths, and are not absorbed by the ozone layer. UVA plays an important role in the formation of Vitamin D in our skin; however, prolonged exposure allows the radiation to penetrate deep into the skin and causes premature aging and immune system problems.

UVB (280-320 nm): These are medium-length UV wavelengths, and are partially absorbed by the ozone layer. UVB is the primary cause of sunburn, and causes damage at the cellular level by affecting our DNA. As the ozone layer thins, more UVB radiation reaches the Earth's surface.

UVC (100-280 nm): These are the shortest UV wavelengths, and are completely absorbed by the ozone layer in the atmosphere.

So UVC is the shortest and the most energetic and would, therefore, technically be the most harmful to us, but since it cannot get through the ozone layer, it does not really affect us. UVA can get through the ozone, but it is the longest, and so it is the least harmful. UVB is more harmful than UVA, and some of it can get through the ozone layer, so it is the one that we are most affected by when we go outside.

Harmful Effects of UV Radiation

UV radiation causes harm to cells by making changes to their DNA. DNA contains four bases (A, T, C, and G), which always pair the same way in normal DNA. A always pairs up with T, and G always pairs up with C.

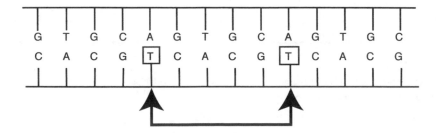

When UV light is absorbed into your skin, it can damage your DNA in a very specific way. If you have two Ts that are close to each other in the same strand of DNA, and UV light hits them, it can change their structure so that they let go of the As they are paired with and they pair with each other instead, causing the DNA between them to pouch out. This new pair, which consists of two Ts, is called a dimer, more specifically a thymine dimer (T is short for thymine), and these dimers are a form of **mutation** (a change, or mistake, in the DNA).

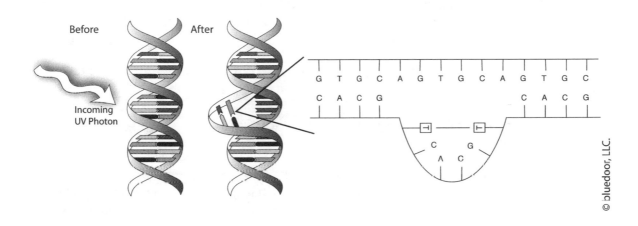

These dimers are a big problem for the cell when it is trying to copy its DNA and divide to make more cells. The machinery that copies the DNA in a cell before it divides cannot work normally in the area where the dimer is located.

Cells have developed special repair systems that work specifically to correct these dimers, and they put a lot of energy into constantly repairing these errors, which occur often because we are exposed to UV regularly. Some of these systems break the bond between the two Ts that make up the dimer, so that they can pair normally again with the appropriate As. Other systems cut the dimer and some of the DNA around it right out of the DNA and then fill in a new, correct piece.

The cell works very hard to make these corrections, but if it can't fix them all before the affected area of the DNA is copied, you can cement in a mutation (a "mistake" in the sequence). Eventually, these mutations can accumulate and lead to cancer, or the death of the cell.

There are people who are born with defects in these DNA repair systems, and they suffer from a genetic disease called xeroderma pigmentosum (XP for short). It is a devastating disease that is characterized by extreme sensitivity to sunlight. It causes freckling, an extraordinarily high rate of skin cancers, and eye damage. Basically, individuals with this genetic disorder cannot go outside during the day. They have to be protected especially from UV, but can really only be exposed to generally low levels of all types of light.

What is Cancer?

So we said that these mutations in the DNA can cause cancer, but how do they do it? All cells have a set lifespan. You can think of each time a cell divides as one year of its life. So if a cell is supposed to live until age 50, it will divide 50, times and after the 50th division, a death signal will be triggered in the cell. This signal tells the cell that its time is up, and the cell will then kill itself.

When a cell becomes cancerous, some mutation has disrupted the gene that codes for the suicide signal and the cell doesn't kill itself. It keeps dividing forever. The cell forgets how to die, and becomes immortal. An immortal cell will continue to divide and produce more cells that are identical to it (containing the same mutation), which also don't know how to die. Then these other cells will divide and produce more identical, immortal, cancerous cells. As these cells build up and continue to multiply, you begin to form tumors. So cancer is basically uncontrolled cell growth due to a mutation in the DNA (like a dimer caused by UV, for example).

There are immune cells in your body that can hunt down these cancer cells and kill them but once a cell becomes cancerous, it tends to continue to mutate in other ways that let it hide from the immune cells. And so the cancer develops further, which can lead to the death of the individual.

So in sum, UV radiation causes mutations ("mistakes") in the DNA, which can cause a gene to function improperly and lead to skin cancer (uncontrolled cell growth).

Skin Cancer and Other Damaging Effects of UV Radiaion

Skin cancer is one of the major diseases of our time. One in five Americans will develop mutations that lead to skin cancer, and every hour one American dies from the disease. Even though people who always burn, never tan, and are fair with red or blonde hair, green or blue eyes, and freckles have a greater chance of developing skin cancer, dark-skinned individuals can also acquire this disease. Skin cancer takes on many forms. There can be various signs, including an asymmetrical mole (common moles are round and symmetrical), a sore that does not heal, a skin growth that increases in size, and a spot that continues to itch, hurt, or scab.

UV radiation can lead to other health defects, as well. Chronic exposure to the sun causes premature aging, which over time can make the skin become thick, wrinkled, and leathery.

Cataracts are a form of eye damage in which a loss of transparency in the lens of the eye clouds vision. If left untreated, cataracts can lead to complete blindness. Research has shown that UV radiation deforms the proteins in the lens of the eye and increases the likelihood of certain cataracts. In addition, it has been found that overexposure to UV radiation may suppress proper functioning of the body's immune system and the skin's natural defenses. All people, regardless of their skin color, might be vulnerable to effects including impaired response to immunizations, increased sensitivity to sunlight, and reactions to certain medications.

Tanning

Tanning beds are not a safe alternative. Tanning is your skin's response to UV light. It is a protective reaction to prevent further injury to your skin from the sun. However, it does not prevent skin cancer. While most tanning beds deliver less UVB radiation than normal sunlight, they contain significantly more UVA radiation. This results in more tanning and less burning, while leading to more UVA damage.

SPF and Sunscreen

The best protection from the sun is to stay out of it. But there are ways to protect yourself when you can't avoid exposure. Sunscreen must be part of your daily regimen. A good sunscreen will act like a very thin shield by absorbing, scattering, and/or blocking ultraviolet rays before they can enter the skin and cause damage. Make sure the sunscreen you choose is effective against both UVB and UVA by looking at the contents. Some common UVA-absorbing ingredients include oxybenzone and dioxybenzone (which are two different kinds of benzophenones) and also avobenzone. The benzophenones only protect against some of the UVA wavelengths, while avobenzone protects against the full UVA spectrum. UVB-absorbing ingredients include para-aminobenzoic acid (PABA), cinnamates, and salicylates all of which cover almost the full range of the UVB spectrum (give or take 10-20 nm).

Sunscreens are labeled with a Sun Protection Factor (SPF) rating. The SPF indicates the amount of exposure time your skin can handle from UVB rays before turning red. For example, an SPF of 4 means that it should take 4 times as long before skin damage occurs.

Suppose your skin begins to redden after 10 minutes in the sun. How long would it take to get burned if you were protected with SPF 4? 8? 15?

4 = 40 minutes   8 = 80 minutes   15 = 150 minutes

Doctors recommend everyone (even those with dark skin) wear a sunscreen with at least an SPF of 15 whenever they are exposed to the sun. SPF relates only to UVB protection. There is no standard for UVA protection in the U.S. Apply sunscreen every 2 hours you are in the sun, or more often if sweating or going in the water. Approximately 1 ounce of sunscreen is needed to cover an average adult from head to toe.

In 2012, the US Food and Drug Administration (FDA) set new requirements for over-the-counter sunscreen products. Only products that protect against all types of sun-induced damage can be labeled "broad spectrum" and SPF 15 or higher. These products not only help prevent sunburn and premature aging, but also reduce the risk of skin cancer. Any sunscreen without "broad spectrum" labeling or with an SPF below 15 has been shown only to protect against sunburn, and not against other risks relating to premature aging or skin cancer. Additionally, sunscreen manufacturers can no longer state their products are waterproof/sweatproof, protect immediately upon application, or that protection lasts longer than 2 hours without reapplication since these phrases overstate product effectiveness. Sunscreens may be labeled water resistant, but must state the protection duration as only 40 or 80 minutes.

What are some other ways to protect yourself from UV radiation?

Getting sunglasses

EXPERIMENT 1

For the purposes of this lab, we will test the UV protection given from the following products: cheap and expensive sunglasses, lip balm, T-shirt material, hand lotion, and sunscreen.

Ultraviolet sensitive beads will serve as markers by which we will determine the level of protection given. The beads show how much UV energy is present by changing from white to purple when exposed to UV-rays. The final part of the experiment is to test the SPF numbers of different sunscreen lotions. By noticing how much time it takes for the beads to change color, you can determine how much UV protection the sunscreen offers.

Which products do you think will offer the best protection against UV damage?

~~Sunscreen~~ clothing

Which products do you use consistently?

clothing

Most UV sources can damage eyes and skin. Be sure that the UV source is set up in a way that minimizes exposure. This includes placing the light below eye level in a housing that directs the light downward and blocks all other rays. If a housing is not used, the use of eye protection (UV-blocking glasses) and a UV shield must be implemented.

Procedure 1

1. Get a divided petri dish, and place UV-sensitive beads on either side.

2. Hold the lens of a cheap pair of sunglasses over one end of the petri dish.

3. Leave the other end exposed (it will serve as our control).

4. Place the petri dish underneath the UV source for approximately 2 minutes. Note the color of the shaded side.

Do cheap sunglasses block UV light?

yes

5. Repeat Steps 1 through 4 three more times using expensive sunglasses, T-shirt material, and lip balm (coat the beads) to shade one side of the petri dish.

How well do these products provide protection against UV radiation?

Not good since they will were damged
by UV light

Do expensive sunglasses offer better protection than the cheap pair?

Yes

Procedure 2

1. Get a divided petri dish, and place UV-sensitive beads on either side.

2. Cut a piece of plastic wrap big enough to cover the top of the petri dish.

3. Cover your petri dish and label it with a waterproof marker as shown:

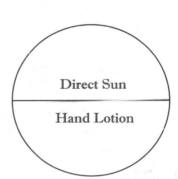

4. Use a cotton swab to evenly spread hand lotion over one side of the petri dish, leaving the other side bare.

5. Place the petri dish underneath the UV source.

6. With the aid of a stopwatch, determine the time of protection given by the hand lotion.

7. Repeat Steps 1 through 5 three more times using sunscreens with SPF 4, 8, and 15. Show your results in the table below.

	Start Time	Finish Time	Time of Protection
Hand Lotion:	2:54	2:56	2
SPF 4:	2:54	2:56	2
SPF 8:	2:54	2:58	4
SPF 15:	2:54	2:59	5

EXPERIMENT 2

For the purposes of this lab, we will test the lethal effects of UV radiation on ordinary baker's yeast (*saccharomyces cerevisiae*). Yeast are simple, unicellular fungi that contain genes for DNA repair that are similar to ones found in humans. Therefore, we can use yeast cells to demonstrate the harmful effects of UV radiation on our own DNA. When exposed to UV light, mutations are created in the yeast DNA, which cause the cells to die. This sensitivity to UV radiation allows us to observe the amount of DNA damage that occurs when cells are either exposed or protected.

Most UV sources can damage eyes and skin. Be sure that the UV source is set up in a way that minimizes exposure. This includes placing the light below eye level in a housing that directs the light downward and blocks all other rays. If a housing is not used, the use of eye protection (UV-blocking glasses) and a UV shield must be implemented.

Procedure 1

Protective Effects of Sunscreen on Yeast

Three groups will prepare one plate each of a normal yeast strain to be exposed to UV light for 1 minute. Each group will be assigned a different SPF rating to protect their yeast (SPF 5, 15, or 45). The TA may also prepare a plate that will not be exposed to any UV to demonstrate how to properly streak a plate, and to use later for comparison to the exposed plates, if desired.

1. Make sure that your hands and work area are clean.

2. Plug in and turn on your UV source to allow the bulb to start warming up while you prepare your plate.

3. Obtain a petri plate of sterilized media (make sure the lid remains closed) from the TA. Keep the plate upsidedown.

4. On the bottom of the petri plate, along the edge, use a permanent marker to write the time and day of your class, along with the SPF rating that your group has been assigned to use (e.g., SPF5 Tues @ 9).

5. Now obtain a sterile swab to spread your yeast. The TA will provide a tube, containing a yeast solution. Dip the swab into the tube and spread the yeast onto the agar inside the petri plate by gently rubbing the applicator back and forth along the surface. Be sure to cover the whole plate with it and to press lightly or you will gouge the agar.

6. Be careful not to touch anything besides the yeast solution and your agar with your swab. Make sure that nothing other than the yeast-dipped swab touches your agar. This will help to prevent contamination with bacteria or other fungi.

7. Set the plate aside (closed and upsidedown), and dispose of the contaminated swab in the appropriate waste container provided by the TA.

8. Cut a piece of plastic wrap large enough to cover the top of the petri plate. Turn your plate right side up, and drape the plastic wrap over the lid. Be sure that your plastic wrap is as flat and spread out as possible to prevent creases that the sunscreen can't cover. Use a permanent maker to trace along the outer edges of the plate so you will know where you put the sunscreen when you remove the saran wrap.

9. Spread small amounts of the sunscreen with your assigned SPF evenly over the plastic wrap, using a sterile swab or your finger. Be sure to spread the sunscreen well. You should not be able to see any sunscreen on the plastic wrap. It should look clear, just as it would if you rubbed the sunscreen in until it disappeared on your skin.

10. Remove the plastic wrap from the petri plate lid, open the lid, and drape the saran over the open plate using the circle that you drew to line up the sunscreen-covered portion of the saran correctly over the plate. Pull it taut around the sides to keep it from hanging down and touching the surface of the agar or you will contaminate the plate. DO NOT let the plastic wrap touch the surface of your agar or you will contaminate your plate!!!

DO NOT look or put any body parts under the foil covering the UV box while the light is turned on!!!

11. Turn OFF the UV source, and place the petri plate inside. Using a watch or a clock in the lab to time yourself, turn on the UV source, and expose the plate for 1 minute.

12. When the exposure is over, carefully remove the plastic wrap (DO NOT let it touch the agar!!!), replace the lid, and give your plate to your TA.

13. The TA will incubate the plates upsidedown at 30° C for 2-3 days to allow the yeast to grow. Results will be viewed at the next class meeting, and should be recorded in the spaces provided below.

Do you think all the sunscreens were effective in protecting the yeast cells? If not, give your predictions.

No, I don't think it's 4

of 18 wl

How do sunscreens protect yeast cells?

they block light from reaching it

As the ozone layer becomes even more depleted, what actions must we take to ensure our safety?

Higher spf, more clothing

Results

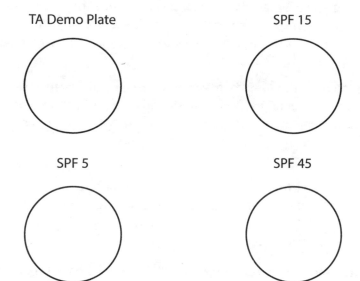

TA Demo Plate

SPF 15

SPF 5

SPF 45

How did your results compare with your predictions about how effectively the different sunscreens used would protect the yeast?

It protects it a little, but still som growth

It is often said that using a sunscreen with an SPF greater than 15 does not provide any additional protection. Based on your results, do you believe that this is true?

No, it seemed to provide more

References

FDA Sheds Light on Sunscreens. Information on the effectiveness of different types of sunscreen and the terminology allowed on sunscreen products.
http://www.fda.gov/downloads/ForConsumers/ConsumerUpdates/UCM258910.pdf

Sunscreens, Tanning Products, and Sun Safety. Information on sunscreens, tanning products, and sun safety intended to help consumers make informed decisions about sun protection and tanning.
http://www.cfsan.fda.gov/-dms/cos-220.html

The Skin Cancer Foundation. Descriptions and photographs of different types of skin cancers.
http://www.skincancer.org/index.html

Sunscreen: the ABCs of Sun Protection. FDA suggestions for sunscreen use and application.
http://www.fda.gov/Drugs/ResourcesForYou/Consumers/BuyingUsingMedicineSafely/ UnderstandingOver-the-CounterMedicines/ucm239463.htm#bottom

The Sun, UV, and You. Information about UV radiation and stratospheric ozone, health risks from exposure to UV radiation, and the UV index.
http://www.epa.gov/sunwise/SUNUVU.PDF

Ultraviolet Radiation: How it affects life on Earth. Web page that includes a UV radiation fact sheet.
http://www.earthobservatory.nasa.gov/Library/UVB/

What is UV? Information on the different categories of UV radiation and the effects on the ecosystem.
http://www.titan.srrb.noaa.gov/UV/what.html

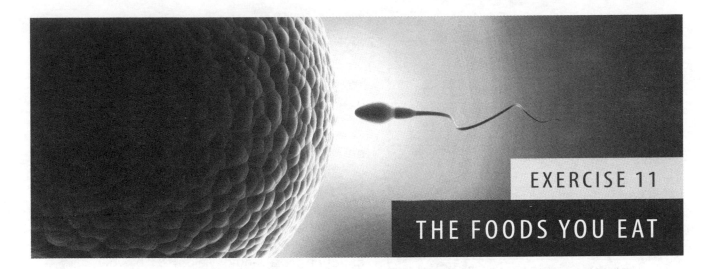

Objectives

In this lab, you will learn to evaluate the foods you eat in order to maximize proper nutrition. Specifically, you will

1. Learn to properly read food labels

2. Be introduced to the main nutritional components in food

3. Calculate your Basal Metabolic Rate

4. Learn to use the food plate as a nutritional guide

5. Measure serving sizes of various foods

6. Analyze nutrition information in certain fast foods

7. Keep a three-day food diary to recognize eating habits.

INTRODUCTION

Nutrition is the study of the foods we eat and their associated nutrients. The foods we consume provide us with the energy and nutrients required for basic bodily functions and performance of daily activities.

If you were to look at the label of any packaged food, you would see a list of the nutrition information describing the main components of that food item. Below is an example of the nutrition label from a 16 oz. box of Rotini pasta noodles.

Nutriton Facts		
Serving Size 3/4 cup (56 g dry)		
Servings Per Container 8		
Amount Per Serving		
Calories 210	Calories from Fat 10	
		% Daily Value*
Total Fat 1g		**2%**
Saturated Fat 0g		0%
Cholesterol 0mg		**0%**
Sodium 0mg		**0%**
Total Carbohydrate 42g		**14%**
Dietary Fiber 1g		4%
Sugars 2g		
Protein 7g		
Vitamin A 0%	Vitamin C 0%	
Calcium 0%	Iron 10%	
Thiamine 30%	Riboflavin 15%	
Niacin 20%	Folate 25%	

* Percent Daily Values are based on a 2,000 calorie diet. Your daily values may be higher or lower depending on your calorie needs:

		Calories:	2,000	2,500
Total Fat	Less than		65g	80g
Sat Fat	Less than		20g	25g
Cholesterol	Less than		300mg	300mg
Sodium	Less than		2,400mg	2,400mg
Total Carbohydrate			300g	375g
Dietary Fiber			25g	30g

Calories per gram:
Fat 9   Carbohydrate 4   Protein 4

According to this nutrition label, there are 8 servings within the 16 oz. box of pasta. Each serving size is approximately 3/4 of a cup. The nutrition information listed below is for one serving only. If you were to have 1 1/2 cups of pasta (2 servings), you would have to double all of the nutrition amounts. For example, you would have consumed 420 calories and 84g carbohydrates. The percent daily values are based on a 2,000 calorie diet, which is simply an average number of calories a person consumes per day. If you were following a 2,000 calorie diet, eating 3/4 of a cup of rotini pasta would yield 14% of your daily allotment for carbohydrates. The bottom of the food label lists the maximum amounts of fat, cholesterol, sodium, carbohydrates, and fiber following both a 2,000 and 2,500 calorie diet. Each of these components and their relevance to healthy nutrition is described below.

Calories

The amount of **calories** in a food item indicates how much potential energy is available in that food. Calories are broken down in the following manner:

> 1 gram of carbohydrate is equivalent to 4 calories

> 1 gram of protein is equivalent to 4 calories

> 1 gram of fat is equivalent to 9 calories

Calories are burned through metabolic processes. Enzymes break down carbohydrates into glucose and other sugars. Fats are broken down into glycerol and fatty acids. Proteins are broken down into their constituent amino acids. These molecules are transported via the blood stream to body cells so metabolic functions can occur.

The quantity of calories necessary for cellular functions varies from person to person. Many factors such as age, gender, height, weight, and activity level contribute to a person's daily caloric requirement. To determine how many calories your body needs per day, you need to calculate your **Basal Metabolic Rate** (**BMR**). This is the amount of energy required for your body to maintain itself. This does not take into account your activity level throughout the day. Essentially BMR, which is the amount of energy needed for your body to function at rest. You are going to calculate your BMR using the Harris-Benedict formula.

Procedure 1

Calculating Basal Metabolic Rate

If you do not already know your body weight in pounds, weigh yourself on the scales provided in lab.

Body weight in lbs. __175__

If you do not know your height in inches, measure yourself with the tape measure or height chart provided in lab.

Height in inches __79__

What is your age? __18__

If you are male, perform the following calculation:

$$66 + (6.3 \times \text{body weight}) + (12.9 \times \text{height}) - (6.8 \times \text{age in years}) = 2065.2$$

(handwritten above terms: 1102.5, 1019.1, 122.4)

If you are female, perform the following calculation:

$$655 + (4.3 \times \text{body weight}) + (4.7 \times \text{height}) - (4.7 \times \text{age in years}) =$$

What is your BMR? __2065.2__

1. Is this a sufficient number of calories for you to consume on any given day? Explain your answer.

   No, this is calculated for being at rest, if I perform any physical activity I will need to consume more calories.

It is important to determine how many calories you need to perform your daily physical activities because BMR only tells you how many calories are required for your body to function at rest. The amount of calories burned in any given activity is dependent upon your individual body weight. This is why most treadmills and cardiovascular equipment ask you to enter your body weight before beginning exercise.

The **Thermic Effect of Food** is the last factor in determining how many calories you need daily. This is the amount of calories burned during the process of digesting food. To calculate the thermal effect of food, multiply the total number of calories you consume in a day by 10% (or .1).

2. Given what you have just learned, how would you determine your total required daily caloric intake?

   2065.2 × .1 = 206.52, then add that to recommended calories

3. What happens when you consume more or less calories than your body burns?

Excess calories will be stored, but if you don't get enough you will lose weight.

Fats

Nutrition labels often break "Total Fat" down into, **saturated fat**, **polyunsaturated fat**, and **monounsaturated fat**. The latter two are both unsaturated fats. At room temperature, saturated fats, such as lard or shortening, are normally solids, whereas unsaturated fats, such as vegetable oil, are liquids. Generally, unsaturated fats are considered to be healthier than saturated fats.

When fats are ingested, they are broken down into **glycerol** and **fatty acids**. These two components are then reassembled into **triglycerides**, which can enter the bloodstream. Triglycerides are absorbed by muscle cells or adipose cells (fat cells) for storage, or are immediately burned as "fuel".

Though excessive fat storage can be unhealthy, fat consumption is a necessary component to our diets. There are several reasons for this:

1. Certain vitamins are only available through fats.

2. Fatty acids cannot be generated by the human body.

3. Fatty acids can only be obtained from food.

4. Fats are a good source of energy.

One pound of fat in the human body is equivalent to 3,500 calories.

1. How many calories are in one gram of fat? 9

2. Based on caloric intake alone, if you wanted to gain 5 pounds, how many extra calories would you have to consume? 15000

3. If you wanted to gain this weight in a time period of 2 weeks, how many extra calories would you have to consume per week? 8750

4. Based on caloric intake, alone, if you wanted to lose 10 pounds in a time period of 8 weeks, how many fewer calories would you have to consume per week? 4375 How many fewer calories per day? 625

Cholesterol

Cholesterol is an important nutritional component because it provides several vital functions.

1. It forms and maintains cell membranes.

2. It assists in the formation of sexual hormones.

3. It produces bile salts that aid digestion.

4. It is converted to vitamin D when skin is exposed to sunlight.

Approximately 1,000 mg of cholesterol is produced in your liver and body cells per day. This is all the cholesterol we actually need. Approximately 85% is **endogenous,** meaning it is produced within our bodies. This is our blood cholesterol. The remaining 15% of cholesterol in our bodies comes from food. This is dietary cholesterol, and comes primarily from meat, seafood, and dairy products.

Why is cholesterol considered to be problematic for the American diet?

Cholesterol can clog your artues

According to the American Heart Association, we should limit our intake of cholesterol to less than 300 mg per day.

You may be familiar with the terms "**Bad Cholesterol**" and "**Good Cholesterol**". These terms refer to the type of carrier molecules that transport cholesterol in the body. Carrier molecules are called **apolipoproteins**. Apolipoproteins are necessary because fats and cholesterol are not water soluble, and do not dissolve in blood. When apolipoproteins are joined with cholesterol, they produce lipoproteins. Bad cholesterol is the low-density lipoprotein (LDL). This is the main carrier of cholesterol in the blood. High levels can lead to blocked arteries and serious cardiovascular risks. Good cholesterol is the high-density lipoprotein (HDL). This has the opposite effect on blood vessels, and can actually help to clear arterial blockages.

Levels of LDL, HDL, and total cholesterol are all indicators for the risk of heart attack and

atherosclerosis. People with total cholesterol levels greater than 275 are at serious risk of developing these and other heart diseases. A cholesterol level below 200 is desirable. Several factors influence a person's cholesterol level. These factors include diet, weight, age, genetics, lifestyle, and disease. Eating foods high in saturated fats and cholesterol greatly increase dietary cholesterol levels. Only foods containing animal products have cholesterol in them. Though vegetable-derived foods do not have cholesterol, if they are high in saturated fats, they can still be unhealthy.

There are several ways to reduce high cholesterol. The best way is to eat a low-fat, low-cholesterol diet and to keep your total fat consumption to less than 30% of your daily caloric intake. Further, saturated fats, such as chocolate and butter, should comprise less than 1/3 of your total fat intake. Also, to reduce your fat and cholesterol intake, limit your consumption of meat, fried foods, and dairy. Eat a variety of different vegetables, fruits, pastas, and grains. Paying attention to nutrition information and regularly reading labels when making food choices is a vital step to eating healthy.

What is another non-diet-related practice that may help you reduce your cholesterol level?

go into the sun to reduce cholesterol

Sodium

The minimum daily sodium requirement for adults is 500 mg. Sodium intake should never exceed 2,400 mg. Sodium is important for several bodily functions. It is involved in active transport of substances across cell membranes, and it helps muscles and nerves function properly. Sodium is abundant in many processed foods. Excessive intake of sodium can lead to health problems including hypertension and edema (swelling of bodily tissues).

List several foods that are high in sodium:

French fries, fast food

Carbohydrates

Simple and complex carbohydrates provide your body with the "fuel" to perform daily functions. Glucose is made up of carbon and water ($C_6H_{12}O_6$) and is the simplest carbohydrate. It is stored in the liver as **glycogen**. Cells absorb glucose and convert it into **ATP** (adenosine triphosphate), the energy required to do cellular work. Fructose, the main sugar found in fruit, is also a simple sugar. Glucose and fructose are both examples of **monosaccharides**. These simple sugars can be absorbed into the bloodstream directly through the intestinal lining.

Disaccharides are simple sugars containing two monosaccharides. Some examples of disaccharides are sucrose (common table sugar) and lactose (the sugar found in milk). These must be broken down into their constituent monosaccharides by enzymes in the digestive tract before entering the bloodstream.

Complex carbohydrates are commonly known as "**starches**". These are long chains of glucose molecules bonded together. Grains, such as wheat, rice, potatoes, and corn, are high in starch. When we consume complex carbohydrates, they are broken down during digestion into their component glucose molecules before they can enter the bloodstream.

What do you think would take longer to digest, a Hershey's bar or a serving of spaghetti? Why?

Spaghetti, It is made up of starches which must be broken down before entering blood stream

Dietary Fiber

Dietary fiber refers to the items we eat that cannot be digested by the human body. Three fibers we eat on a regular basis include **cellulose, hemicellulose** and **pectin**.

Cellulose is a complex carbohydrate and is the structural component in plants. Hemicellulose can be found in the hulls of various grains such as wheat and bran, and pectin is found in fruits. When we eat fiber, it is not digested, and passes untouched through our excretory systems. As a result, fiber helps bodily wastes pass through the colon more rapidly. Consuming 25 to 30 grams of fiber per day is recommended.

What might be some potential health benefits from eating a high-fiber diet?

Helps bodily wste psor mor quickly

Proteins

Proteins are chains of **amino acids**. Amino acids are the essential building blocks of cells. Our bodies are constructed by approximately 20 different amino acids. There are two different types of amino acids in our bodies, **essential** and **non-essential amino acids**. Essential amino acids can only be obtained through food, whereas non-essential amino acids can be created from other chemicals in the body.

In our diet, proteins come from both plant and animal sources. Most animal sources, such as meat and dairy, provide "complete protein". Complete proteins contain all the essential amino acids. Vegetable sources often contain low amounts of, or are lacking in certain essential amino acids. However, different vegetable sources contain different essential amino acids. By eating a variable diet, all essential amino acids are easily obtained. The current recommended daily allowance for protein is about 0.36 grams of protein per pound of body weight.

How much protein should you be consuming on a daily basis? _63 gram_

Vitamins

Vitamins are organic substances required in minute quantities for nutrition. Vitamins can act as coenzymes in the regulation of metabolic processes. Some vitamins can be produced within the human body. Others are obtained only by consuming natural foods. Some common required vitamins are listed in the table below:

Vitamin	Name	Vitamin	Name
Vitamin A	Retinol	Vitamin D	Calciferol
Vitamin B1	Thiamine	Vitamin E	Tocopherol
Vitamin B3	Niacin	Vitamin K	Menaquinone
Vitamin B6	Pyridoxine		Folic Acid
Vitamin B12	Cyanocobalamin		Panthothenic Acid
Vitamin C	Ascorbic Acid		Biotin

Fresh, natural foods generally provide all the necessary vitamins. Food processing often destroys the naturally occurring vitamins. That is why many processed foods are "fortified" with man-made vitamins, instead.

Minerals

Minerals are elements required by the human body to create specific molecules for bodily functions. Some necessary minerals include

Calcium	Copper	Iron	Molybdenum	Selenium
Chlorine	Flourine	Magnesium	Phosphorus	Sodium
Chromium	Iodine	Manganese	Potassium	Zinc

These minerals are all provided in the foods we eat. Like vitamins, if we lack certain minerals in our diets, associated health problems may arise.

Choose one of the vitamins or minerals listed above. Describe what function it serves in the human body, and list an associated health risk that can result from a deficiency in that vitamin or mineral.

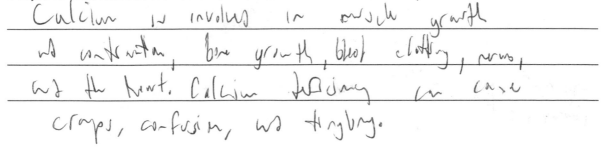

Calcium is involved in muscle growth and contraction, bone growth, blood clotting, nerves, and the heart. Calcium deficiency can cause cramps, confusion, and tingling.

The old USDA Food Pyramid has been replaced by a plate icon.

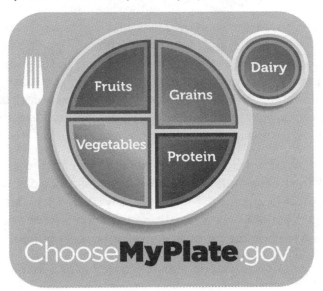

The foods we eat are complex mixtures of various macromolecules, vitamins, and minerals that supply our bodies with raw materials and energy. Food must be digested before most nutrients are available to build and power cells. And so the saying goes, *"You are what you eat."*

The ChooseMyPlate.gov web site is very informative and emphasizes strategies for building a healthier plate.

- at least half your plate should be fruits and vegetables
- maximize whole grains
- cut back on empty calories; foods high in fat and added sugar lack essential nutrients
- be physically active and match your caloric intake with your activity level

Online Resources to Assist Your Diet Analysis

WebMD Food-o-meter
www.webmd.com/diet/healthtool-food-calorie-counter

MyFoodDiary.com (Free for 7 days)

Nutrition Data
www.Nutritiondata.self.com
You need to register and create an account, but there is no charge.

Procedure 2

Analysis of Serving Sizes and Food Plate Interpretation

The following foods will be available in your lab:

* Do not eat any of these foods!

Bread	Apples	Carrots	Peanuts	Potato Chips
Cereal	Grapes	Tomato Sauce	Eggs (Hard Boiled)	Butter Spray
Noodles	Orange Juice	Milk	Soybeans	Crackers
Green Beans	Cheese	M&M Candies		

Divide into five groups. Your lab instructor will assign one of the food groups from the food plate to each lab group. From the foods available in lab, pull out the foods that belong in the food group you were assigned. Look at the food labels on each of your food items to separate out their proper serving sizes. Again, examine the food plate, and look at the section marked Food-A-Pedia. You will divide out the maximum number of servings for your food group (e.g.) Complex carbohydrates 11, fruits 4, etc.). Depending on how many serving sizes you need, you may need to separate multiple servings of the same food. You should, however, have at least one serving of each of your food items separated out. Your instructor will demonstrate serving sizes for the "fats and sweets" group. Measuring cups and balances will be provided for those foods requiring measurements.

Be sure to document the nutrition information for each serving. When each group has completed separating serving sizes, work together as a class to devise a menu plan for a day. Using the serving sizes your class has already separated, arrange them on an empty lab bench to demonstrate the menu plan. When completed, you will have a visual representation of what a full day's food allowance should be if you were to consume the maximum allotted servings from each food group.

In the spaces provided, write in your sample menu, and work together as a class to construct the nutrition information for the day.

Sample Menu:

Meal	Food	Calories	Fat	Cholesterol	Sodium	Carbs	Fiber	Protein
Breakfast	eggs J	210	15 g	585 mg	125 mg	3 g	0	18 g
	Blikcaberry	50	0 g	0 mg	0	10 g	2 g	<1 g
Snack								
Lunch	½ pub sub	430	13 g	60 mg	1320 mg	89 g	3 g	30 g
Snack	15 carb	180.5	9.2 g	0	153.0 mg	21.9	5.1	5.9 g
	1 tbsp penut btr							
Dinner	burger	200	9 g	70 mg	800 mg	4 g	0	25 g
	fried fry	380	19 g	0	266 mg	48 g	0	5 g
Snack	apple	130	0	0	0	34 g	0	1 g
Total		1530.5	65.2	655	2644.3	209.9	10.1	85.9

x9
~~~~~~~~
586.7

x4
=839.6 +

x4
=343.6
1770

Remember that there are 4 calories per gram of protein and carbohydrate, and 9 calories per gram of fat. Multiply your total carbohydrates and proteins by 4. Multiply your total fat by 9. Add these three numbers together to calculate your total caloric intake. This number may not match your total calories column because food companies often round their nutrition information. Below, list how many calories came from fats, proteins, and carbohydrates. List your total caloric intake. Next, calculate the Percent Caloric Intake. Divide the calories from fat by the total caloric intake. Multiply this by 100. Repeat this process for calories from protein and calories from carbohydrates to calculate their percent caloric intakes.

Calories from fat ___586.0___   % from Fat ___3.1%___

Calories from Protein ___743.6___   % from Protein ___5.1%___

Calories from Carbs ___839.6___   % from Carbs ___2.1%___

Total Caloric Intake ___1770___

1. Given what you have learned in today's lab, is this a healthy menu? Why or why not?

___No, we aren't getting enough calories___

___per day in this menu___

2. Does your menu plan meet the guidelines set by the USDA food plate?

~~No, fat too high this~~ Yes, the guidelines are met

3. Take a moment to look at the individual serving sizes. Are they larger or smaller than you would have estimated them to be?

___Smaller, we didn't count the calories___

___you ate or over eat___

4. How do these serving sizes compare to the serving sizes you generally eat during a meal?

___Similar to what I might actually___

___eat___

In our everyday lives, it is impractical to measure out all our food servings, unless we are required to do so for medical reasons. Therefore, it is useful to recognize serving sizes without always having to measure. Examine the serving sizes in your sample menu. Can you think of objects that might be useful references for approximating serving sizes in the future? For example, a single serving of meat is comparable in size to the back of your fist (not counting your fingers). For each of the food examples below, list a "frame of reference" that may help you remember the proper serving size when measuring equipment is not available.

Cereal ___bowl___   Block Cheese ___half hatful___

Peanuts ___fill up your fist___   Grapes ___hatful___

Carrots ___2 hatfuls___   Butter ___Spoonful___

5. What might be the incentive for food companies to market small serving sizes?

If its unhealthy + the body

values will be less

Procedure 3

Analysis of Fast Foods

In this procedure, we are going to compare and contrast the nutritional components of various menu items from several fastfood restaurants. Look up the nutrition information for each menu item found on your lab bench. Record the calories, Fat (g), Fat (%), Cholesterol (mg), Sodium (mg), Carbohydrates (g), and Protein (g) for each food.

Hamburgers

McDonalds

Cheeseburger   Serving Size __1__
Calories _205_ Fat __13g__ Fat (%) __20__ Cholesterol __40 mg__
Sodium _750 mg_ Carbs _26y_ Protein _15 g_

Burger King

Cheeseburger   Serving Size __1__
Calories _587_ Fat __15 g__ Fat (%) __2.3__ Cholesterol __33 mg__
Sodium _1167_ Carbs _43y_ Protein _20 y_

Pizza

Dominos

Ultimate Deep Dish-cheese only (14")   Serving Size __1__
Calories _240_ Fat __16g__ Fat (%) __25__ Cholesterol _25 mg_
Sodium _670 mg_ Carbs _26y_ Protein _12_

Pizza Hut

Pan-cheese only   Serving Size __1.__
Calories _245_ Fat __11y__ Fat (%) __17__ Cholesterol __0__
Sodium _757_ Carbs _28y_ Protein _11y_

Sub Sandwiches

Subway

Super Roast Beef Sandwich (6")   Serving Size __1__
Calories _410_ Fat __28y__ Fat (%) __43__ Cholesterol _125_
Sodium _2230mg_ Carbs _17 y_ Protein _51y_

Blimpie

Roast Beef Sandwich   Serving Size __1__
Calories _360_ Fat __13__ Fat (%) __20__ Cholesterol __0__
Sodium __0__ Carbs _34_ Protein _26y_

1. Why does the nutrition information differ for similar food items? List several possibilities.

   cuyu is make different

2. For each food item, which restaurant do you think had the healthiest option? Why?

Hamburgers: _Burgr Bng, too much fat_

Is this really a healthy food option? Why or why not?

No, but it had a lot less fat

Pizza: _Papa, what too much fat_

Is this really a healthy food option? Why or why not?

No, it had a lot less fat

Sub Sandwiches: _Roosh Bus Subwch, too with fat_

Is this really a healthy food option? Why or why not?

No, too much fat

Now we will examine different menu items within the same fastfood restaurant (Wendy's). Before looking up the nutrition information, write down which food item you think is the healthiest option. Look up the nutrition information, and record it the spaces provided. Then analyze the nutrition information to determine what actually is the healthiest of the three foods listed.

Wendy's

Of the three foods listed, which do you think would be the healthiest option?

Taco Salad w/o dressing
Calories ___60___ Fat ___3___   Fat (%) ___5___   Serving Size ___155 g___
Sodium ___160___ Carbs ___5___   Protein ___4___   Cholesterol ___0___

Chicken Ceasar Pita w/ dressing
Calories ___480___ Fat ___19___   Fat (%) ___29___   Serving Size ___217 g___
Sodium ___1190___ Carbs ___48___   Protein ___30___   Cholesterol ___60___

Grilled Chicken Sandwich
Calories ___530___ Fat ___30___   Fat (%) ___46___   Serving Size ___208 g___
Sodium ___940___ Carbs ___35___   Protein ___30___   Cholesterol ___90___

1. Which menu item do you think is the actual healthiest option? Why?

   Taco Salad, way less sodium

2. Did your initial choice differ from the actual healthiest menu option?

   No, I guessed the taco salad

3. Is fast food safe to eat often? Why or why not?

   No, it is very unhealthy

Procedure 4

3-Day Food Dairy

This exercise will not be completed in lab. You will conduct this for yourself at home, and turn this in to your instructor in your next lab. You will be keeping a food dairy for three days to help you recognize your eating habits. For each day, you will fill out the following tables:

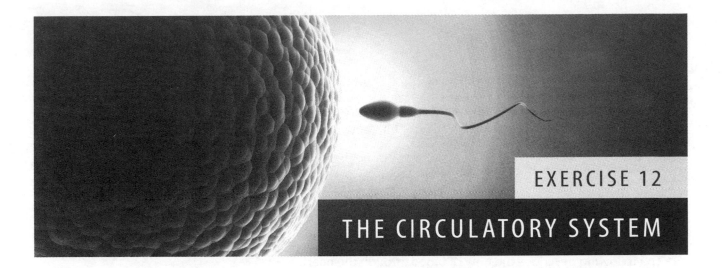

THE CIRCULATORY SYSTEM

Objectives

The objectives of this exercise are to become familiar with the flow of blood using figures and heart specimens provided in lab; to understand the implications of hypertension, and to determine blood pressure using a sphygmomanometer; and to determine heart rate recovery time following limited exercise.

INTRODUCTION

Listen to your heart. The repeated thumps indicate that the heart is pumping blood through your body. The heart is a muscular pump that is controlled by electrical impulses. If your heart stops beating, the essential cellular requirements stop being taken to (nutrients and gasses) and from (waste materials from metabolism) the cells, resulting in the death of body tissue. The heart makes sure that the surrounding tissue remains constant by circulating fluid throughout the body. The circulating fluid is the blood, a liquid that flows in two circuits: the **pulmonary** and **systemic systems**. The pulmonary system involves the heart pumping oxygen-poor blood to the lungs, where oxygen is taken up and carbon dioxide is given up. The oxygenated blood then flows back to the heart. In the systemic system, oxygenated blood is pumped from the heart to the rest of the body and back. Besides oxygen, the blood carries **nutrients**, **vitamins**, **proteins**, **lipids**, and **hormones** throughout the body.

Your heart pumps approximately 15,141 liters (4,000 gallons) of blood through your body each day. However, the heart itself does not receive any nutrients from the blood it pumps. Instead, it receives its own supply of blood (and nutrients) through the **coronary arteries**. Most heart attacks occur due to blockage of one or more of the coronary arteries, thus blocking the blood flow that supplies the heart muscle itself.

Procedure 1

Heart Structure and Blood Flow

Find your pulse, and count how many beats there are per minute. Write this down.

_105_ per/min.

Calculate how many beats per hour _6300_ beats/per/hr.

Calculate how many beats per day _151,200_ beats/per/day.

Calculate how many beats in a week _1,058,400_ per/week.

The following describes the flow of blood through the heart:

- Deoxyginated blood - superior and inferior vena cavas - right atrium - right ventricle - pulmonary arteries - lungs

- Oxygenated blood - lungs - pulmonary veins - left atrium - left ventricle - aorta - to the rest of the body

Now look at the diagram of the heart and the heart your instructor is demonstrating. Pay particular attention to location and size of the following structures:

Right atrium	**Right ventricle**	**Left atrium**	**Left ventricle**
Aorta	**Superior vena cava**	**Inferior vena cava**	

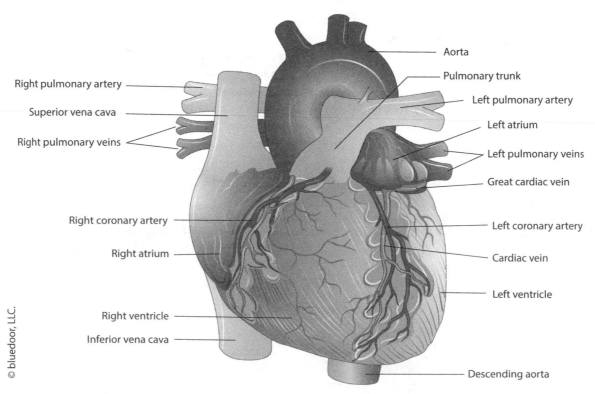

Figure 1: Anterior view of the human heart.

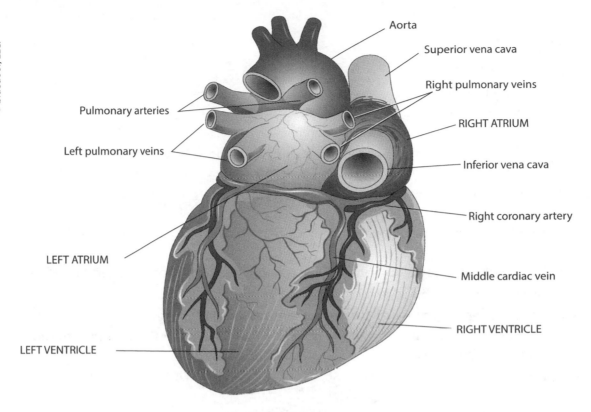

Aorta

Superior vena cava

Right pulmonary veins

Pulmonary arteries

RIGHT ATRIUM

Left pulmonary veins

Inferior vena cava

Right coronary artery

LEFT ATRIUM

Middle cardiac vein

LEFT VENTRICLE

RIGHT VENTRICLE

Figure 2: Posterior view of the human heart.

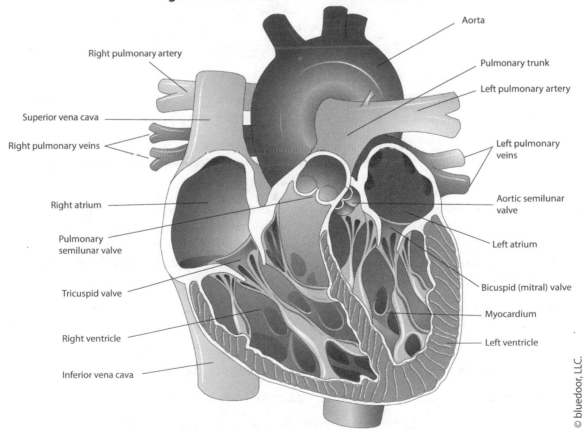

Aorta

Right pulmonary artery

Pulmonary trunk

Left pulmonary artery

Superior vena cava

Right pulmonary veins

Left pulmonary veins

Right atrium

Aortic semilunar valve

Pulmonary semilunar valve

Left atrium

Tricuspid valve

Bicuspid (mitral) valve

Myocardium

Right ventricle

Left ventricle

Inferior vena cava

Figure 3: Interior view of the human heart.

Dissection Terms

Anterior: front position.

Posterior: back position.

Superior: upper position.

Inferior: lower position.

Sulcus: grooves on the surface of the heart ventral walls.

Auricle: during a phase of heartbeat, the atria is empty of blood and becomes smaller. This produces the appearance of a wrinkled pouch on the anterior surface of each atrium, called the auricle.

Superior vena cava: upper vessel on the right atrium. It transports deoxygenated blood to the right atrium from the head and arms.

Inferior vena cava: Lower vessel that empties deoxygenated blood from the trunk and legs into the right atrium.

Pulmonary trunk: large vessel for transporting deoxygenated blood from the heart to the lungs.

Aorta: carries oxygenated blood to the entire systemic system.

Interventricular septum: connective tissue between right and left ventricle.

Tricuspid valve: valve that detoxified blood passes through. Three flaps that pass from the right atrium to right ventricle.

Pectinate muscles: posterior wall is smooth, while the anterior wall is rough, because of these muscles.

Myocardium: muscular portion of the wall of cardiac muscle.

Procedure 2

Heart Dissection

1. Retrieve a preserved sheep heart, dissection tray, dissecting instruments, probe, and hand protection, if desired. Rinse the heart with cold water to wash off excess preservatives or blood.

2. Before starting to cut, it is important that we first orientate ourselves with the heart. We start by locating the apex (point) and the base (blunt) of the heart.

3. Locate the ventricle chambers using the figures provided. Once you have located both chambers, give them a gentle squeeze. One will be harder and feel more solid. This is the left ventricle because it performs a greater workload and needs extra-muscular walls. The left ventricle pumps blood for systemic circulation, while the right side pumps blood for pulmonary circulation.

4. Identify the aorta and pulmonary trunk extending from the superior section of the heart. The pulmonary trunk is more anterior and may be seen breaking off into left and right pulmonary arteries.

5. Locate the left and right auricles, which are earlike flaps on top of the atrial chambers.

6. Find the superior vena cava located at the superior end of the right atrium.

7. Now place the heart into the anterior position, as seen in **Figures 1 and 3**.

8. Again locate the superior vena cava, and cut along its left wall down to the right atrium. The cut should finish at the tricuspid valve, between the right atrium and ventricle. Try to observe the valve.

9. Now continue with the cut until you reach the interventricular septum, marked by lighter–colored tissue between the ventricles.

10. Try to locate the pectinate muscles along the walls of the right atrium. These muscles are extended outward, making the surface rough and comb-like. (Pectin means comb.)

11. Identify the large opening of the inferior vena cava, located on the ventral atrial wall.

12. Continue the cut line all the way around the heart until you reach the top of the left atrium.

13. Observe the different thicknesses of the cardiac muscle, or myocardium, in the ventricles. Also compare the two cavities.

14. Notice the entry point of the pulmonary veins into the left atrium.

15. Now using the Circulation Scheme of the human body, try to follow the path of blood through your specimen. Using a probe to follow and identify parts of the heart will help to distinguish similar-looking sections.

16. Compare the atrial and ventricular cavities one last time before properly disposing of the heart. Make sure your lab area is clean for the next group to use when you are finished.

Circulation Scheme of the Human Body

Right atrium

through the tricuspid valve

to the right ventricle

through the pulmonary semilunar valve

to the pulmonary trunk

to the right and left pulmonary arteries

to the capillary beds of the lungs

to the pulmonary veins

to the left atrium of the heart

through the mitral/bicuspid valve

to the left ventricle

through the aortic semilunar valve

to the aorta

to the systemic arteries

to the capillary beds of the tissues

to the systemic veins

to the inferior vena cava and superior vena cava

entering the right atrium of the heart.

Note the difference in sizes between the right and left ventricles. What accounts for the difference in sizes?

_____

_____

What would happen if there was a hole between the left and right atrium?

_____

_____

_____

Why are there valves between chambers of the heart?

_____

_____

_____

Arteries have thick walls, and veins have thinner walls. Why do you think that is necessary?

_____

_____

Describe your ideas about the difference between arteries, veins, and capillaries. Which would you expect to have valves and why? Compare your ideas to those of your partner.

_____

_____

_____

Procedure 3

Heart Beat and Blood Pressure

Now that you've seen a heart and understand the flow of blood, you are going to study the activity of your own heart.

Our bodies are continually attempting to maintain an internal balance, or **homeostasis**. We looked at one aspect of homeostasis, the regulation of blood sugar and insulin. By quantifying the amount of glucose in various popular soft drinks, we were able to see just how much sugar we consume when ingesting a small amount of these drinks, thus affecting our insulin levels.

Another component in many soft drinks is **caffeine**. Caffeine is both a **stimulant** and a **diuretic** (increasing the secretion and flow of urine). How do you think caffeine affects homeostasis?

It negatively affects it, it make your urine secretion increase

How would caffeine, as both a **stimulant** and a **diuretic**, affect heart rate?

It would raise heart rate

Using the stethoscope found on your bench, listen to your partner's heart beat.

The sound you hear is the "LUB, DUB, LUB, DUB" of blood being pumped through the heart. The LUB sound corresponds to the closing of the **atrioventricular valves** at the beginning of systole. **Systole** refers to systolic, which is defined as the phase of the heartbeat in which the ventricles contract to force blood into the arteries. The DUB is the closing of the **semilunar valves** at the start of diastole (see **Figure 11.3**). **Diastole** refers to diastolic, which is defined as the phase of the heartbeat that is between two contractions during which the heart muscle relaxes and fills with blood. The sounds you are hearing are your partner's heartbeat while resting. Count how many times the LUB DUB sound occurs in 1 minute.

_105_

To more accurately measure the flow of blood, you can measure blood pressure. Specifically, you can measure the amount of pressure exerted on the walls of the various vessels throughout the body as blood flows. People with **low blood pressure** (or hypotension) have trouble maintaining enough pressure in the blood vessels to complete the entire circuit of blood flow. This condition is much less common, and often less life threatening, than **high blood pressure** (or hypertension). High blood pressure means that too much pressure is being exerted on the blood vessels, causing them to weaken. High blood pressure is often caused by a narrowing of the blood vessels due to plaque formation.

Take your partners blood pressure.

Find the pulse spot at the joint of the lower and upper arm (the brachial artery). Place a pen mark there.

Put the blood pressure cuff around the upper arm. Be careful, however; if it hurts your partner, it is too tight, and your reading won't be accurate.

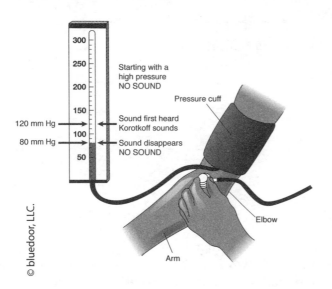

Put the stethoscope onto the marked spot. Inflate the cuff to around 160 or 180 mm mercury, as seen on the gauge. This pressure closes the artery, and a sound of each pulse is heard.

Slowly release the pressure in the cuff by carefully opening the air valve. As soon as you hear the beat, note the pressure on the gauge. Continue releasing the pressure slowly, and, as soon as you no longer hear the beat, note the reading on the gauge. When no sound is heard, there is insufficient pressure on the cuff to compress the artery.

© bluedoor, LLC.

Figure 4: Use of a sphygmomanometer to measure blood pressure.

Now have your partner take your blood pressure, and record the measurement below:

Pressure at which the first beats were heard _____113_____ = systolic pressure

Pressure at which last sounds were heard _____72_____ = diastolic pressure

Blood pressure is measured by systolic pressure over diastolic pressure, e.g., 120/80, which is the "normal" human blood pressure.

Each of you should practice taking blood pressure a few times until you are completely sure you can get a good reading.

Procedure 4

Effects of Exercise

At the beginning of the lab you took your resting pulse rate. Record it here:

 bpm

While your partner times you, beginning running in place (or similar exercise) and continue for 3 minutes. When the 3 minutes is up, **immediately** have your partner take your pulse. Your partner should continue taking your pulse every **2 minutes** for the next **10 minutes**, or until your heart rate is back to normal. This is called the "recovery time". Record your pulse rate in **Table 1**.

Table 1: Number of heartbeats per minute following three minutes of exercise.

Time (min)	0	2	4	6	8	10
BPM	~~90~~	~~77~~	58			

Switch off and time your partner while he/she exercises for 3 minutes. Follow the same procedures listed above.

Compare your recovery time to your partner's. Was it longer? Was it shorter? If it was different, what might explain the difference?

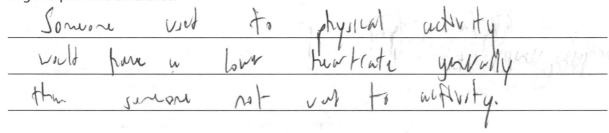

Someone used to physical activity would have a lower heartrate generally than someone not used to activity.

The more exercise you do, or the healthier you are, the faster your recovery rate will be. Why?

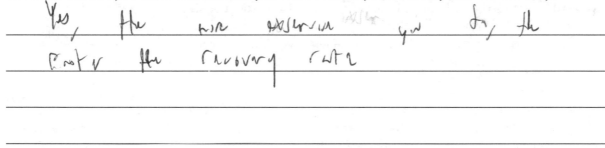

Yes, the more exercise you do, the faster the recovery rate

What is happening in terms of blood flow, rate, and volume of blood going through your heart when you exercise?

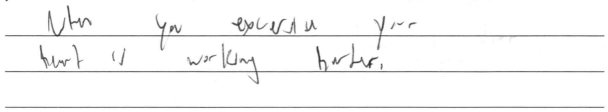

When you exercise your heart is working harder.

Certain drugs and chemicals are known to increase your heart rate. Other than caffeine, name three things that you might eat or drink that could increase your heart rate without doing exercise:

Soda, sugar, and   spicy   food

_____

_____

_____

Arteries are moving blood **away from the heart** 100% of the time. Almost always, arteries carry **oxygenated** blood to the tissues, except for the **pulmonary arteries**. The pulmonary arteries are the only arteries that carry **deoxygenated** blood. They carry blood from the right ventricle (away from the heart) to the lungs. Veins carry blood **to the heart** 100% of the time. They almost always carry deoxygenated blood, except for the pulmonary veins. Pulmonary veins are the **only** veins that carry oxygenated blood. They carry blood from the lungs to the left atrium (to the heart). The sites of gas exchange occur around the **capillaries**, the smallest blood vessels in our body. Here, diffusion occurs; the high concentration of oxygen in the blood moves toward the lower concentration of oxygen in the tissues. Also, carbon dioxide is diffused from the tissues to the blood. Capillaries around the **alveoli**, small, grape-like sacs in our lungs, diffuse the waste, carbon dioxide, into the alveoli to be exhaled. At the same time, oxygen is moving from the alveoli into the blood. This oxygenated blood is returned to the heart, and the cycle starts again. Oxygen helps break down glucose, which is used to make **ATP**, cellular energy. Without ATP, you couldn't blink, breathe, or pump blood. This is why it is so important that we can breathe and that our circulatory system works well.

The heart is a double pump that serves two circulations. The right side of the heart pumps blood through the pulmonary circuit to the lungs and back to the left heart. (Note: The diagram simplifies things. The actual number of two pulmonary arteries and four pulmonary veins is reduced to one each in the diagram.) The function of this pulmonary circuit is strictly to provide for gas exchange. The second circuit, which carries the oxygen-rich blood, supplying functional blood supply to all body tissues, is called systemic circulation The left heart pumps blood by way of the systemic circuit to all body tissues and back to the right heart. The blood flowing through the pulmonary circuit gains oxygen and loses CO_2. Blood flowing through the systemic circuit loses oxygen and picks up CO_2.

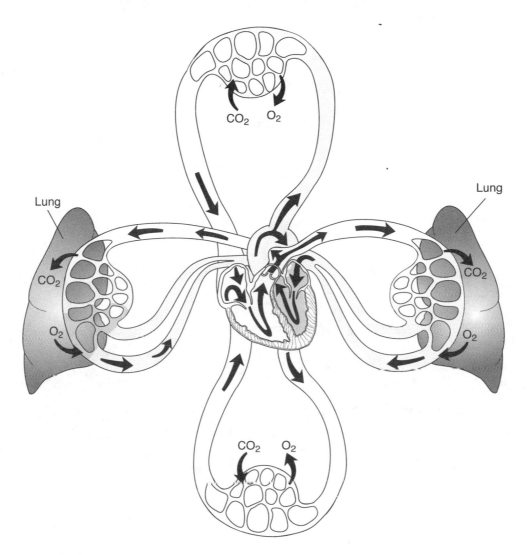

THE SYSTEMIC AND PULMONARY CIRCUITS

Label the above diagram with the following:

Pulmonary Circuit

Systemic Circuit

Pulmonary Arteries

Pulmonary Veins

Aorta

Vena Cavae

Capillary Beds

Left and Right Atria-

Left and Right Ventricles

Color oxygen-poor/CO_2-rich blood BLUE

Color oxygen rich/CO_2 -poor blood RED

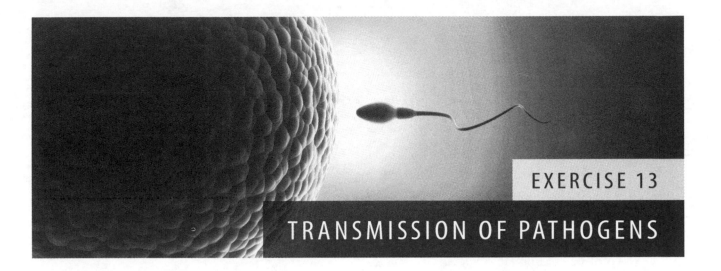

TRANSMISSION OF PATHOGENS

Objectives

The objectives of this exercise are to become familiar with the science of epidemiology; to learn the categories of disease reservoirs, modes of disease transmission, types of carriers, and portals of entry into the body; to define patterns and extent of disease using the terms endemic, epidemic, pandemic, morbidity, and mortality; to become familiar with different types of pathogens and show experimentally how they are spread through direct contact, as well as to determine the origin of infection; to learn the causative agents, symptoms, prevention, and cure, if any, of most sexually transmitted diseases.

INTRODUCTION

Our ancient ancestors recognized that disease spread from one person to another. Diseases that marked people with highly visible conditions, such as leprosy, caused victims to be shunned and labeled by society. Lepers were often required to wear bells or continually cry "Unclean!" in a loud voice to warn others of their presence. During outbreaks of highly infectious diseases, such as smallpox, bubonic plague, and influenza, people fled in terror from the center of the diseased area, often spreading infection further afield.

The science of **epidemiology** or the study of the origin, cause, and spread of disease actually began during the cholera epidemic in London in the mid-1800s, when John Snow, a local physician, began to infer from his own study and data collection that the disease was associated with the water supply from regions of the Thames, heavily polluted with untreated sewage. From his study, it gradually became apparent that disease, poverty, and filthy living conditions contributed to the spread of diseases like cholera and typhoid, and that statistical evidence could provide information that was useful in stopping or preventing epidemics.

In order to study epidemiology, there is some important terminology associated with categories of disease reservoirs.

Reservoir – the place in nature where the disease (organism) normally lives or is found in significant numbers.

Zoonoses – reservoirs of diseases in animals that can be transmitted to humans.

Inanimate – secondary or accidental reservoirs on non-living material.

Modes of transmission refer to how disease is spread between hosts. Epidemiologists must understand the many ways that pathogens, or infectious agents capable of causing disease, spread.

- **Direct Contact** – may be person to person, or reservoir to person.

- **Fomites** – inanimate objects.

- **Vectors** – insects that spread infectious agents.

- **Carriers** – humans or other animals in which the infectious agent is growing or reproducing with no apparent harm to the host. **Chronic carriers** are organisms that have had the disease, but from whom the infectious agent has not been completely purged. The organism no longer causes a disease state in the host, but remains a potentially infectious agent to another organism. Also, some organisms carry potentially virulent pathogens as normal flora or naturally non-infective to the host, which may be potentially pathogenic to others. **Transient carriers**, however, are organisms "coming down" with a disease, but who haven't shown identifiable symptoms, and those who are recovering from the disease.

- **Portals of entry** – ways or places an infectious agent must enter a host to establish the disease. The major portals of entry are:

  ❐ Gastrointestinal tract

  ❐ Anal intercourse

  ❐ Urogenital tract

  ❐ Respiratory tract

  ❐ Puncture wounds

  ❐ Eyes or hair follicles

- **Nosocomial** – infections contracted during a hospital stay, carried either by patients, personnel, or inanimate objects.

- **Compromised host** – individual whose general health condition makes him more susceptible to infectious agents. These conditions include immunosuppressant therapy, trauma, injury, surgery, stress, diabetes, and other serious illnesses.

Using the terminology you learned above, describe the situation below:

Clostridium tetani, which causes tetanus or lockjaw, has its reservoir in the soil. What type of reservoir is this? _____

A patient contracts antibiotic-resistant *Staphyloccus aureus* resident in the nostrils of a surgical scrub nurse. Mode of transmission? _____

Years after contracting Hepatitis B, the infectious antigen remains in the bloodstream of infected individuals, preventing them from being suitable blood donors. _____

The infectious agent causing dengue fever is carried by a mosquito. _____

The etiological agents of tuburculosis, chicken pox, and measles are resistant to drying and are easily spread through air. _____

The new treatments for AIDS allow HIV-positive people to maintain a "healthy" appearance for a longer period of time, although they remain capable of spreading the virus. _____

A student has had the flu, but feels well enough to return to school to take his exam only because he's over the "worst of it." _____

Epidemiologists study disease transmission in terms of number of victims and number of lives lost. _____

The term **endemic** refers to disease that is normally found in a particular area. For example, AIDS is now endemic in most countries in the world, as is malaria in many countries in the southern hemisphere. When an outbreak of disease spreads suddenly in a particular place or area, it is called an **epidemic**. An example of an epidemic is the cholera outbreak in Mexico and Bolivia. An epidemic that involves a large portion of the population in the world is known as a **pandemic**. The flu is often pandemic. With the increasing potential for world travel, pandemics pose more of a threat than ever before.

The Center for Disease Control is a U.S. federal organization that tracks both morbidity and mortality of infectious disease or the **pathogens**, the agents, that cause disease. **Morbidity** refers to the number of people who catch the disease, whereas **mortality** refers to the number of people who die from the disease. Epidemiologists must search for clues not only to find the origins of disease, but its modes of transmission and treatment. Their approach to breaking the cycle of infection involves

- **Identification** of those with the disease and the pathogen (virus, bacteria, fungus, protozoan, or other parasite).

- **Elimination** or control of the reservoir.

- **Immunization** or making the host resistant.

- **Preventing transmission** by quarantine, restricting travel, sanitation, mass immunization, elimination of vectors.

- **Maintaining hygenic conditions** in the water, food supply, etc., and training of personnel.

To simulate a disease spread by direct contact, the following lab exercises will demonstrate the spread of infection after exchange with 3 individul contacts, and then 4 individual contacts. Note the differences.

Procedure

1. Obtain a numbered test tube containing a clear solution. One test tube contains a basic or "infected" solution; the others contain plain water. Each solution has a different number. It is important that you take the solutions in order; the first person will take solution #1, the second will take #2, and so on. Record your number:

    Stock Solution # _____

2. Using a clean plastic pipette, transfer 3 full pipettes of your solution to a clean test tube. Make sure you mark this test tube with the same number as your stock solution. If your solution turns pink, your test tube is contaminated, and you must pour your solution down the sink and thoroughly rinse out your test tube.

3. Choose one person at random and exchange one pipette-full of your solution with that person; fill your pipette, wait for the other person to fill their pipette, then exchange simultaneously. Record their solution number as the first contact below.

4. Repeat the procedure two more times, so that you have exchanged one pipette-full of your solution with three different people in the classroom.

    # of 1ˢᵗ Contact: _____   # of 2ⁿᵈ Contact: _____   # of 3ʳᵈ Contact: _____

5. After everyone has completed three exchanges, throw away your pipet. Have your solution tested for infection by using the base indicator. All of the solutions started out as plain water, except for the "infected" solution. All of the solutions that have become infected, as well as the original infected solution, will have pink or fuchsia color after the indicator is added. Those who have not been obviously infected will have solutions that remain clear.

6. Record the color or your solution: _____. Pour your solution down the sink, then thoroughly rinse your test tube 6 times and invert it in the test tube rack.

7. Those who have an obviously infected solution will list their solution number in the table on the board under infected solutions, and write the numbers of their first, second, and third contacts in the appropriate columns.

8. Record the class data in **Table 1**, and answer the questions that follow.

Table 1: Class result from direct contact with a pathogen after exchange with three individuals.

Infected solutions	First contact	Second contact	Third contact

1. What is the total number of people who participated in this simulation? _____

2. Knowing that there was only one host for the epidemic, what was the maximum number of people in the lab that could be infected after each contact?

   First contact: _____ Second contact: _____ Third contact: _____

3. Could fewer than the maximum number of individuals be infected? If so, how?

   _____

   _____

4. Which stock solution do you think was the original host for the epidemic? Why do think so?

   _____

   _____

5. Did anyone in the classroom exchange their solution with an infected individual, but did not test positive? How can you explain that?

   _____

   _____

   _____

Get a clean pipette and repeat the exercise, but this time exchange with 4 different classmates. Test for infection after everyone has completed their exchanges, and record the results on the board.

Record the class data in **Table 2**.

Table 2: Class result from direct contact with a pathogen after exchange with four individuals.

Infected solutions	First contact	Second contact	Third contact	Fourth contact

6. Did more people test positive for infection? If so, how many more?

_____

_____

7. How many people came into contact with infected individuals, but did not test positive? Were there more than with 3 exchanges?

_____

_____

8. Relate what you have learned from this experiment to your own life. How easily could you become infected with a pathogen through direct contact?

_____

_____

_____

9. What are some preventative measures you can take to avoid coming into direct contact with a pathogen? How about indirect contact, airborne contact, or contact via biological vector?

_____

_____

_____

_____

_____

Sexually Transmitted Diseases

Sexually transmitted diseases (STDs), formerly known as venereal diseases, are infectious diseases transmitted primarily through sexual contact. More than 12 million people in the United States, including 3 million teens, are infected with STDs every year. The United States has the highest STD rate in the industrialized world; roughly one in ten individuals in the U.S. will contract an STD in his/her lifetime. STDs are transmitted by direct sexual contact with infected individuals, the sharing or misuse of infected hypodermic needles, or received through transfusion of infected blood products. Some STDs are passed from an infected mother to her child before (cross placenta), during (in birth canal), or after the birth (in breast milk). And, finally, STDs may be contracted by healthcare workers by accidental puncture from contaminated needles or other sharps and/or contact between broken or damaged skin or mucous membranes with infected body fluids. We will concentrate on the most common STD, current trends, prevention, and control.

Common STDs: Parasitic

Pubic Lice

Pubic lice, *Phthirus pubis*, are arthropods that attach to the skin and hair in the genital (pubic) area. They lay eggs (nits) on the shaft of the hair that can survive for up to seven days, even away from the host, on inanimate objects such as bedding, furniture, towels, and brushes. The lice cannot survive for more than 24 hours away from the body (the host), but are spread by sexual contact from person to person. They are often called crabs because of their microscopic resemblance to small crabs. Symptoms include itching and skin irritation. They may also be detected on the scalp, underarms, and chest hair. Treatment is available over the counter or by prescription, and involves treating all possible sexual partners, as well as their clothing and bedding.

Trichomoniasis

Trichomoniasis is a parasitic infection caused by the protist *Trichomonas vaginalis*. It is commonly referred to as "trich" and is transmitted by sexual contact and rarely by contact with contaminated towels and wet clothing. Trichomoniasis infections are common among the sexually active, including college populations. The symptoms are similar to those of other sexually transmitted diseases. Men may or may not have symptoms, including a thin watery discharge from the penis and burning during urination. Women often have more pronounced symptoms, including genital itching, painful intercourse, burning during urination, abdominal pain, and/or a yellow-brown discharge. Infections of the urethra or bladder sometime occur.

The parasite can be detected during routine urinalysis. *Trichomonas* is a parasite with a whip-like flagellum and often an active undulating motion is seen in the urine sediment. Treatment consists of Flagyl or metronidazole, an oral antibiotic, which should be taken by anyone having sexual contact with the infected individual, regardless of symptoms.

Common STDs: Bacterial

Chlamydia

Chlamydia, caused by the bacterium *Chlamydia trachomatis*, is the most commonly transmitted STD in the United States. Approximately 500,000 new infections are reported to the CDC per year; however, because chlamydia may produce no symptoms, it is estimated that its true incidence is nearly ten times the number of reported cases. It is estimated that 40 percent of men and 85 percent of woman have no symptoms. When symptoms do develop, about 5-10 days after infection, men may experience burning or painful urination or discharge from the penis. Women may have vaginal discharge, burning urination, or mild abdominal pain, but if left untreated, chlamydia damages the reproductive tissue causing PID, pelvic inflammatory disease. PID can cause chronic pelvic pain, infertility, or fatal complications in pregnancy. In men, the urethra and possibly the testicles may become inflamed, potentially causing sterility. Chlamydia is also the leading cause of neonatal conjunctivitis, an eye infection of the newborn that can cause blindness.

Chlamydia infections are diagnosed by testing penile and vaginal discharge for the presence of the bacteria. Both symptomatic and asymptomatic sex partners should be treated. It is easy to treat with the antibiotics tetracycline and doxycycline, and even easier to avoid. Using the male or female condom, limiting the number of sex partners, abstinance, and getting routine checkups for sexually transmitted diseases are means of avoiding chlamydia.

Gonorrhea

Gonorrhea, caused by the bacteria *Neisseria gonorrhoeae*, infects the membranes lining certain genital organs. Experts estimate approximately 850,000 new cases of gonorrhea appear annually in the United States. Like chlamydia, gonorrhea is often undetected, but men are more likely to develop symptoms than are women. Whether the disease manifests symptoms or not, gonorrhea is extremely contagious. Symptoms include burning and painful urination and penile or urethral discharge. Long-term complications in men include epididymitis and, eventually, sterility. Approximately 2% of persons with untreated gonorrhea may develop DGI, disseminated gonococcal infection, characterized by fever, skin lesions, and arthritis. Untreated gonorrhea can cause PID in women, infertility, ectopic pregnancy, abscesses, and sometimes sterility. Babies born to mothers with gonorrhea are at risk of infection during delivery, and often develop eye infections caused by the bacteria.

Gonorrhea can easily be treated with the antibiotics doxycycline or ceftriaxone; however, resistant strains are becoming more common. Bacterial smear and culture of penile or vaginal discharge is necessary for diagnosis. If there is no discharge, cultures from the urethra, throat, or rectum may yield positive results, as well as recent advances in DNA/PCR testing, which require a urine sample. All sex partners, with and without symptoms, should be treated. Abstinence from both genital and oral sex is the only way to be 100% protected from gonorrhea. If sexually active, the use of condoms, monogamy, or limited sex partners, and regular checkups for sexually transmitted diseases are essential.

Syphilis

Syphilis is a potentially life-threatening STD. It is caused by the bacteria, *Treponema pallidum*, and although it is less common on the college campus than chlamydia or gonorrhea, there are still an estimated 100,000 new cases in the United States every year. In the early (primary) stage of syphilis, a genital sore, called a chancre, develops shortly after infection and disappears on its own. The second stage, which usually involves a skin rash anywhere on the body, usually begins approximately two months after the initial infection. The rash can sometimes persist over an entire year. Syphilis then enters a latent stage, in which there are usually no symptoms and bacterial replication is minimal. This is the tertiary stage. Finally the fourth stage, which occurs 5 to 30 years after infection, sometimes produces lesions anywhere on the body, dementia, or blindness. If the disease is not treated, the infection can progress over years, affecting the brain, heart, meninges, and vertebrae. It can be devastating to the fetus during pregnancy, causing deformity and death, and most pregnant women receive screening for the disease during the first weeks of pregnancy to avoid complications. Syphilis can be treated with penicillin in the primary, secondary, and latent stages.

Syphilis can be diagnosed by one of many blood tests used to screen for it. It must be confirmed by another method, since false positives do occur. *Treponema pallidum* is a difficult bacteria to culture, so direct techniques are not often used for diagnosis, but to rule out other diseases. Transmission of the disease may occur through sexual contact between moist mucous membranes, or from the sharing of hypodermic needles, blood transfusions, or from the transmission of disease from infected mother to her unborn fetus.

Common STDS: Viral

Herpes

Genital herpes is caused by infection with the herpes simplex virus (HSV). Most cases of genital herpes are due to HSV type 2; however, some cases of genital herpes are also caused by HSV type 1, a common cause of cold sores. Genital herpes causes recurrent outbreaks of painful sores on the genitals, although the disease often remains dormant with no symptoms for long periods of time, with the virus in its latent stage resident in the ganglia, clusters of nerve cells. From time to time, the virus can be reactivated, traveling down the nerve to the skin's surface, where it multiplies and causes similar lesions, usually in a similar location to the original outbreak. A recurrence can be triggered by any of the following (also known to trigger oral herpes outbreaks): surgery, illness, stress, fatigue, sunburn, diet, or vigorous sexual intercourse.

Herpes is spread by direct contact to the skin. If you have active genital herpes, and you have intercouse, you can give your partner genital herpes. If you have a coldsore on your mouth, and have oral sex with your partner, you can give your partner genital herpes. Herpes is most likely to be spread when a sore is present, but can also be spread between viral outbreaks, when no signs or symptoms are present. Preventing self infection is easy. Wash your hands to prevent spread to the eyes and other body areas. Use condoms to help prevent the spread of herpes during sexual intercourse. Herpes can cause serious complications for pregnant women, including premature birth and spontaneous abortions. The baby may be infected through the placenta or during delivery. Infants infected with HSV may have central nervous system damage. Vaginal delivery is contrindicated during an outbreak of the herpes virus on the genitalia. Cesarean section may be indicated if a mother tests positive for herpes. Viral culture can be done when symptoms are present, or the blood can be tested by Western Blot for the presence of HSV 1 or 2. Blood is not routinely screened for HSV 1 because of its common association with oral herpes, but if you have recurring genital herpes, and are not seropositive for type 2, you probably have HSV 1.

Although there is no cure for herpes, some drugs have been effective in reducing the duration and frequency of outbreaks. Antiviral therapy and immunotherapy are being examined today. L-lysine is an amino acid that appears to be an effective agent for the reduction of occurrence, severity, and healing time for recurrent HSV infection. At this time, the most effective means of preventing herpes infection is abstinence and/or any of the various barrier forms of contraception, such as the male and female condom.

Human papilloma virus

Genital warts, transmitted by the human papilloma virus during sexual contact, grow on the penis and in and around the vagina and anus. They can be found on the cervix, vagina, and vulva, and sometimes look like small cauliflowers, but also may be flat and hard in appearance. The CDC estimates that there are one-half to one million new cases of genital warts in the United States per year. Although they are relatively painless, genital warts, or condylomas, significantly increase the risk of cervical cancer in females. Cellular changes may result in intraepithelial neoplasia, a precancerous condition of the cervix. They are treatable with many topical medications, cryotherapy, laser, liquid nitrogen, and can be removed with minor surgical procedures. Genital warts, however, cannot be cured. Yearly PAP smears provide the physician with information regarding cervical health that may help in the prevention and treatment of cancer.

Acquired immunodeficiency syndrome (AIDS)

AIDS is an incurable and deadly STD that results from infection with the human immunodeficiency virus. AIDs attacks the body's immune system, leaving victims open to a wide range of opportunistic infections. While HIV can be transmitted by other means, sex is the most common means of transmission, whether it be vaginal, oral, or anal. HIV is transmitted through semen, vaginal secretions, blood contact, and through the placenta or breast milk from mother to child. HIV can be transmitted in blood and blood by-product transfusions if donor unit testing is inadequate. Sharing hypodermic needles, getting tattoos and body piercings at unsafe facilities, and being poked with any HIV-infected sharps, such as dental or surgical instruments, are further examples of blood-to-blood contact that cause the spread of HIV. The spread of HIV, however, is most often associated with **risky behaviors**, such as intravenous drug abuse or unprotected sex, and is clearly an epidemic of worldly proportions.

HIV and AIDs, however, cannot be transmitted by casual contact such as touching, shaking hands, or being close to a person with HIV. There must be an exchange of blood or body fluids for viral transmission. HIV cannot be contracted in a swimming pool or hot tub, nor on a toilet seat, unless under extremely unusual circumstances involving open sores and body fluids. HIV is not transmitted by donating blood, and due to the comprehensive donor screening procedure in the United States, is almost never contracted by receiving blood by transfusion.

It is possible for an HIV-infected individual to be **asymptomatic** for many years, and unknowingly transmit HIV many times to many partners. On average, without treatment, a person progresses from infection to AIDS in about 7 to 10 years. This is a rough estimate that varies somewhat depending on how the individual contracted the disease. In general, the rate of progression is higher for those who are infected through blood contact, rather than through sex, although there are discrepancies. Transfusion recipients, hemopheliacs, and IV drug users may be the fastest to progress, whereas homosexual men tend to progress more slowly. These are generalizations, which may be due to the general state of health of these populations.

AIDS, or the acquired immunodeficiency syndrome, is caused by a virus, which infects and kills immune cells (T-lymphocytes). T-cells initiate many of the body's immune responses. When their number is low, the body's defense against infection is destroyed, and it becomes susceptible to a number of infections. Early symptoms of AIDS include persistent fever, night sweats, swollen lymph nodes, fatigue, weight loss, and loss of appetite. The person may develop white spots in and around the mouth due to infection with yeast. There may be chronic diarrhea, nervous system disorders, vision or hearing loss, and/or memory loss. **Opportunistic infections**, such as PCP, *Pneumocystis carinii*, may develop, which may lead to pneumonia and even death. Other opportunistic infections can be caused by viruses, bacteria, fungi, and other organisms normally resident in the body, that become pathogenic due to the lack of normal immune response. Kaposi's sarcoma is a rare cancerous lesion that often develops on the skin of AIDS patients. The following table summarizes the more common opportunistic infections associated with AIDS and HIV.

Viral infections	Protozoal infections	Fungal infections	Bacterial infections
Cytomegalovirus (CMV)	Cryptospridiosis	Aspergillosis	Salmonella
Hepatitis	Isopsoriasis	Candidiasis	Streptoccus pneumoniae
Genital herpes	PCP	Coccidiomycosis	Haemophilis influenzae
Herpes zoster	Toxoplasmosis	Cryptococcal meningitis	Campylobacter
Molluscum contagiosum		Histoplasmosis	Shigella dysenteriae
Human papilloma virus			

At the present time, there is no cure for AIDS. Early diagnosis and treatment may improve the quality of life, and eliminate or arrest the cancers or opportunistic organisms that invade the HIV-infected body. Antiviral drugs, such as AZT, *zidovudine*, prevent viral replication, but do not kill the virus. Cocktail mixtures of drugs may boost the immune system, but do not cause the disease to go away. Many research dollars are being spent on the treatment of HIV, as well as its detection and prevention. Screening for HIV in high-risk populations involves testing the blood of volunteers for the antibody to HIV, which is resident in the bloodstream of infected individuals from approximately six months after exposure to the remainder of their lives. False- negative results may be obtained with the ELISA screening procedure, and it is recommended that high-risk individuals be retested six months later for verification. Positive results must be again verified by a Western Blot procedure.

So what puts people at risk for contracting such a deadly disease? AIDS is still the leading cause of death in the United States in victims ages 24-45. Already, 19 million people worldwide have died of AIDS, and nearly twice that many are living with HIV. The disease is surely not confined to men who have sex with men. AIDS and other STDs pose a risk for us all. The surest protection against all STDs is sexual abstinence, or the absence of all sexual activity. Mono-gamy, in which two partners do not have sexual relations with anyone outside the couple's relationship, safe sex, and the use of condoms greatly decreases the chance of exposure to HIV and other STDs. There are risky behaviors that increase the chances of contracting HIV and other STDs that should be avoided. These are

- Sex with multiple partners
- Sex under the influence of drugs or alcohol
- Unprotected sex (without a condom)
- The use of lubricants (other than water-based lubricants) with a condom
- Receptive anal intercourse, causing potential tearing and bleeding
- Needle-sharing for drug use, steroids, tatoos, or any reason

Using the information provided above, how would you determine if a sexually transmitted disease is endemic, epidemic, or pandemic?

_____

_____

_____

Which STD is associated with small, flat, hard bumps on the cervix?

_____

What is the treatment or cure?_____

What are some of the physical symptoms associated with syphilis?_____

_____

_____

Are males or females more likely to manifest symptoms of *Chlamydia* infection?

_____

What is an opportunistic infection? _____

_____

_____

_____

_____

Name several examples of opportunistic infections associated with HIV: _____

_____

_____

_____

_____

When you are in a new monogamous relationship, and both test negative for HIV, is it necessary to use condoms as protection? Why or why not?

_____

_____

_____

_____

_____

_____

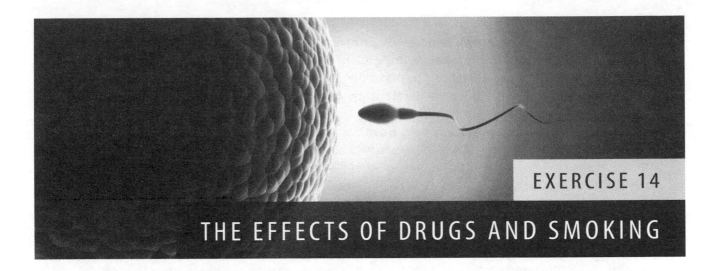

THE EFFECTS OF DRUGS AND SMOKING

Objectives

The objectives of this exercise are to learn the effects of drug use on the human body, and to determine the effects of stimulants and depressants on daphnia heartbeat, to learn what chemicals are in cigarette smoke and why they are harmful, to understand the effects of smoking on different parts of the human body, and to visually inspect the differences in tar output between unfiltered, filtered, and unfiltered "low tar" cigarettes.

INTRODUCTION

Many drugs and chemicals work in the body by either mimicing or blocking the effects of the natural chemicals in the body. Additionally, they may stimulate or block the release of a chemical from the body. Most drugs used to regulate the nervous system act at the synapse level. Neurons pass information to one another across synapses, small spaces that separate two neurons. The four drugs that we will concentrate on for this lab are alcohol, epinephrine, caffeine, and nicotine.

Drugs can be divided into four categories: stimulants, depressants, hallucinogens, and narcotics.

1. **Stimulants:** substances that temporarily arouse or accelerate physiological or organic activity in the body.

2. **Depressants:** also known as sedative-hypnotics, depress or slow down the rate of vital activities in the body.

3. **Hallucinogens:** also known as psychedelics, these are substances that can produce visual, auditory, and tactile distortions in the user.

4. **Narcotics:** drugs that dull the senses, induce sleep, and with prolonged use become addictive.

A person is considered **addicted** when they deviate from normal habits and give themself habitually or compulsively to a substance. **Dependency** is a state of being determined, influenced, or controlled by a chemical substance. The dependency can be **physical or psychological**. When the person thinks he or she needs a chemical substance to function he or she is **psychologically addicted**. If the body suffers from withdrawal symptoms when the chemical substance is suddenly discontinued, the person is **physically dependent**, or **addicted**. Some individuals can build up a **tolerance** to some substances; this is the capacity to absorb a drug continuously or in large doses without adverse effects. This will normally lead to a user turning to stronger, more addictive drugs to reach a state of euphoria, or "high".

Alcohol

When a person drinks ethyl alcohol, it is absorbed into the bloodstream. The alcohol is absorbed by the small intestines and distributed to the entire body through the bloodstream. As the blood passes through the liver, the body tries to fight the effects of alcohol on the body. Enzymes in the liver metabolize it to acetaldehyde, which is a poisonous substance to the human body. The enzyme acetaldehyde dehydrogenase then converts acetaldehyde to acetic acid, a chemical that the body can use as a source of energy (see chain below). People that are unable to metabolize acetaldehyde to acetic acid will have very low tolerance, much lower than an individual who has no problems metabolizing acetaldehyde.

(Chain) *Ethyl Alcohol* » *Acetaldehyde* » *Acetic Acid*

The accumulation of acetaldehyde produces the effects of alcohol intoxication. Intoxication and other effects of alcohol are caused by disruptions of the balance of excitatory and inhibitory neurotransmitter systems. If an individual is unable to convert acetaldehyde to acetic acid at an adequate rate to rid the body of the toxic substance, the user can suffer from alcohol poisoning, which is known to cause death.

Epinephrine

Epinephrine (also know as adrenalin) is a hormone found naturally in the human body that is secreted by the adrenal medulla, the sympathetic nerve endings of the adrenal glands. It is produced by the body in times of stress, and gets the body ready for trauma. It is also used by the body as a neurotransmitter that helps nerves communicate with each other as they transmit messages from one part of the body to another. It is found to have three effects on the human body (1) increase in blood sugar, (2) dilation of blood vessels, and (3) increase in blood pressure.

This hormone catecholamine, stimulates the secretion of glycogen and inhibits the secretion of insulin. Epinephrine markedly stimulates glycogen breakdown in muscles and, to a lesser extent, in the liver. It will tell the body that glucose is scarce. It also stimulates an increase in breathing rate and heart beat rate. Oxygen is taken in and carbon dioxide is given off faster, and the heart sends the blood through the body faster, speeding delivery of extra oxygen to the muscles and hastening removal of wastes. Epinephrine causes blood vessels in the skin and abdominal organs to constrict, decreasing the blood supply to these organs and sending blood that is normally "stored" in these areas into more active circulation. This, in effect, increases the volume of available blood. This trade off of blood supplies helps to maintain the blood pressure. There is not enough blood to fill the whole circulatory system in the dilated state.

Caffeine

Caffeine is found in a variety of plants, and is produced and stored in their leaves, stems, seeds, and roots. It comes from the substance in plants known as caffeic acid. The effects of caffeine on the human body are seen mostly in the central nervous system (CNS), and it is classified as a psychostimulant. It also has effects on the respiratory system, cardiovascular system, gastrointestinal system, kidneys, metabolism, and the muscular system. Caffeine can also increase the body's ability to absorb certain substances and increase or improve the effects of active substances. For example, research has proven that caffeine can increase the effect of Ibuprofen.

Nicotine

Nicotine is rapidly absorbed into the blood and starts affecting the brain within 7-10 seconds. In the cardiovascular system, nicotine increases heart rate and blood pressure and restricts blood flow to the heart muscle. The drug stimulates the release of the hormone epinephrine, which further stimulates the nervous system and is responsible for part of the "kick" from nicotine. It also promotes the release of the hormone beta-endorphin, which inhibits pain.

Experiment 1

For the purposes of this lab we will test the following four substances caffeine, epinephrine, ethyl alcohol, and nicotine to determine their effects on the heart rate of daphnia. Daphnia are members of the phylum Arthropoda and the subphylum Crustacea. Also found in this subphylum are shrimp, crabs, lobsters, crayfish, barnacles, and pill bugs. The daphnia belong to a small suborder of predominantly fresh-water crustaceans that represent an extremely important link in the food chain. They are commonly referred to as water fleas because the planktonic forms perform an unusual jump or hop, followed by a slow sinking movement. Daphnia are perfect for this experiment because they posses a transparent laterally flattened carapace that allows the observer to see the heart beating through the transparent carapase. This will allow the observer to determine if the chemicals that the daphnia are subjected to are depressants or stimulants.

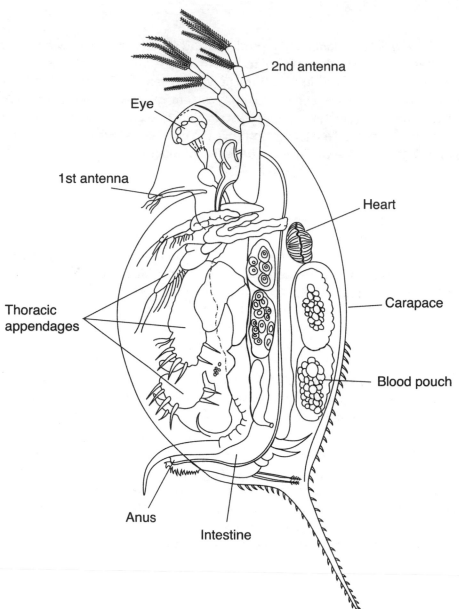

2nd antenna

Eye

1st antenna

Heart

Thoracic
appendages

Carapace

Blood pouch

Anus

Intestine

Questions:

1. What effects do you think depressants and stimulants will have on the heart rate?

_____

_____

2. Before the experiments are conducted, based on the background information, what substances do you think will be depressants and which will be stimulants?

_____

_____

Procedure 1

1. Cut a square piece of daphnia netting, and place it in the bottom of the magnification chamber.

2. Use a pipette to collect 1 or 2 daphnia and place them in the magnification chamber, on top of the netting. Transfer as little water as possible; this will keep the daphnia from swimming.

3. Observe the daphnia by holding the cover of the chamber approximately 2 inches above the chamber. Use the diagram of the daphnia as an aid to locate the heat and familiarize yourself with their anatomy. If the daphnia are too small to see, you can set the bottom half of the chamber on a microscope slide and view it through the compound microscope on low power. (4x). Keep this light source low or the animal will die.

4. Once you have located a daphnia with a viable heartbeat, you must use a stopwatch to time the heartbeats and determine the heart rate per minute. Count the number of beats for 10 seconds, and enter that number in the data table marked control. Then multiply that number by 6 to calculate the heart rate per minute. Repeat this procedure 2 more times and calculate the average heart rate of the daphnia. Enter this data in the data table marked "Control".

Control	# of Heart Beats in 10s	x 6	Heart Rate per min.
Trial 1			
Trial 2			
Trial 3			
Average	Trial 1+Trial 2+Trial 3	÷ 3 =	Average Heart Rate

Procedure 2

Testing Stimulants and Depressants

1. Add a drop of caffeine solution to the daphnia in your magnification chamber. Wait 1 minute for the solution to be absorbed.

2. Once again, time the heartbeat 3 times to calculate the heart rate per min. Then average them together for the average heart rate. Show your results in the table labeled "Caffeine".

Caffeine	# of Heart Beats in 10s	x 6	Heart Rate per min.
Trial 1			
Trial 2			
Trial 3			
Average	Trial 1+Trial 2+Trial 3	÷ 3 =	Average Heart Rate

Questions:

1. Is caffeine a stimulant or a depressant, and why?

_____

_____

2. How much of an increase or decrease was there in the heart rate when compared to the control?

_____

_____

Discard the daphnia from the previous experiment, and rinse and dry the chamber and net. Remember to use a new daphnia for each solution tested. Do a control for each daphnia before adding the solutions. Then repeat Steps 1 and 2 from **Procedure 2**, three more times, using epinephrine, ethyl alcohol, and nicotine. Display your results in the appropriate table.

Control	# of Heart Beats in 10s	x 6	Heart Rate per min.
Trial 1			
Trial 2			
Trial 3			
Average	Trial 1+Trial 2+Trial 3	÷ 3 =	Average Heart Rate

Control	# of Heart Beats in 10s	x 6	Heart Rate per min.
Trial 1			
Trial 2			
Trial 3			
Average	Trial 1+Trial 2+Trial 3	÷ 3 =	Average Heart Rate

Questions:

1. Is Epinephrine a stimulant or a depressant, and why?

_____

_____

2. How much of an increase or decrease was there in the heart rate when compared to the control?

_____

_____

Control	# of Heart Beats in 10s	x 6	Heart Rate per min.
Trial 1			
Trial 2			
Trial 3			
Average	Trial 1+Trial 2+Trial 3	÷ 3 =	Average Heart Rate

Ethyl Alcohol	# of Heart Beats in 10s	x 6	Heart Rate per min.
Trial 1			
Trial 2			
Trial 3			
Average	Trial 1+Trial 2+Trial 3	÷ 3 =	Average Heart Rate

Questions:

1. Is Ethyl Alcohol a stimulant or a depressant, and why?

_____

_____

2. How much of an increase or decrease was there in the heart rate when compared to the control?

_____

_____

Control	# of Heart Beats in 10s	x 6	Heart Rate per min.
Trial 1			
Trial 2			
Trial 3			
Average	Trial 1+Trial 2+Trial 3	÷ 3 =	Average Heart Rate

Nicotine	# of Heart Beats in 10s	x 6	Heart Rate per min.
Trial 1			
Trial 2			
Trial 3			
Average	Trial 1+Trial 2+Trial 3	÷ 3 =	Average Heart Rate

Questions:

1. Is Nicotine a stimulant or a depressant, and why?

_____

_____

2. How much of an increase or decrease was there in the heart rate when compared to the control?

_____

_____

Interpretation of Results

1. Why is it necessary to start with a new daphnia after each substance?

_____

_____

2. Would you expect these chemicals to act the same way in humans? Explain your answer.

_____

_____

3. After determining the effects of caffeine, nicotine, epinephrine, and alcohol on the daphnia heart rate, and based on the information located in this exercise, what effects do you think cocaine would have on heart rate, and why?

_____

_____

4. Compare your results from the four experiments to the results obtained by your classmates. Were your results the same or different? Explain why.

_____

_____

Experiment 2

Smoking and Nicotine

Nicotine addiction is the "most widespread example of drug dependence in our country," according to the U.S. Public Health Service. "A cigarette is a euphemism for a cleverly crafted product that delivers just the right amount of nicotine to keep its user addicted for life before killing the person," says the director-general of the World Health Organization. You might wonder why there is such a negative attitude associated with smoking cigarettes, and why they are so hazardous to your health. The main ingredients are tar, tobacco, and nicotine. You may think that tobacco is just a plant, nicotine is just a stimulant like coffee, and a little bit of tar should be able to be tolerated by the body. However, burning tobacco creates hot, toxic fumes that destroy the lining of air passages. Tar contains many poisonous chemicals that build up on the lung's surface. Nicotine, a more addictive drug than cocaine or heroine, is carried to the brain via the bloodstream within 10 seconds of inhalation.

Cigarette companies are also legally allowed to include additives in tobacco products. Just a few of theses include sugar, cocoa, and menthol. These seem harmless enough, until you understand why they are added. The sweet taste that sugar adds may appeal to younger people. Burning cocoa produces a gas that causes the passages of the lungs to **dilate**, or open up, so that the body can absorb more nicotine. Menthol numbs the throat, allowing the smoke to be more easily inhaled. Lethal chemicals are also found at the tip of a burning cigarette, such as arsenic and formaldehyde.

Less than 7% of smokers trying to quit will last longer than one year without returning to their old habits. The reason for this addiction may lie in nicotine's power to act both as a stimulant and a sedative. Upon exposure to nicotine, the adrenal glands produce **epinephrine**, or adrenaline. This release of adrenaline subsequently causes a release of glucose and an increased heart rate and blood pressure. Nicotine can also exert a sedative effect on the nervous system that can cause a release of dopamine in the regions of the brain that control pleasure. This is the same reaction that occurs with heroine and cocaine use.

Most adults breathe about 15 times per minute, taking in about a pint of air each time air

passes through the lungs. The bronchial tubes carry the air to the site of gas exchange in the lungs, the **alveoli**. The **capillaries** (smallest blood vessels in the human body) around the alveoli diffuse carbon dioxide into the lung to be exhaled then they receive oxygen. Our bodies have a natural defense system to help protect our lungs. The mucus in our air passages traps dust, germs, and pollen before they can get deep within our lungs. Tiny, hair-like structures, called **cilia**, line the air passages and sweep out mucus, germs, and irritants. Coughing, sneezing, and swallowing clear away debris. Smoking destroys the cilia, allowing **carcinogens** (cancer-causing substances) to become imbedded in the lungs.

"It's my body," you say, but smoking cigarettes also affects the environment. One whole tree is used just to cure 30 packs of cigarettes. Cigarette smoke contains carbon monoxide and methane, two main gases that are related to the greenhouse effect. The most widely grown non-food crop on this planet is tobacco. Ten million to twenty million people could be fed if food crops replaced tobacco.

There are a lot of reasons why a person should choose not to smoke. If you are a smoker and choose the low tar option, you may be getting fooled. "Light" cigarettes offer air holes around the filter to allow smoke to escape before it is inhaled. The tobacco companies have machines that smoke cigarettes to test for tar and nicotine levels, but when a real person enters the picture, the levels of tar and nicotine actually being inhaled changes drastically. The holes happen to be so tiny, you can't see them, and when you hold a cigarette between your fingers, you tend to cover them up, negating their purpose.

People who switch to a low tar brand adapt the way they smoke by inhaling more deeply and taking more puffs to intake the same amount of nicotine that their bodies are used to receiving. One problem with inhaling more deeply is the increased possibility of a deep lung cancer, **adenocarcinoma**, recently associated with smoking filtered cigarettes. Adenocarcinoma is different from the kind of cancer found in the large air tubes of patients who smoked non-filtered cigarettes.

Lung cancer is not the only disease a smoker has to look forward to. Smoking is also related to cancers of the larynx, esophagus, bladder, kidney, and cervix. Earlier in this book, we discussed why it is important for your tissues to get oxygen. Oxygen supply is also necessary for the heart to function properly. The chemicals in cigarettes replace space in the lungs normally reserved for oxygen. The heart then has to pump harder and faster to get the same amount of oxygen to the tissues. Making the heart work continually harder may result in hypertension, and can ultimately cause a heart attack. Emphysema, a breakdown in the walls of the alveoli, can also result from smoking. This effect on the alveoli causes a considerable decrease in the amount of oxygen intake.

Procedure 1

The amount of smoke inhaled is correlated to the rate of disease. For this experiment, you will determine how much smoke (tar) different types of cigarettes generate.

Carefully place a filter over the open end of the plastic smoking apparatus container. Gently push down on the white ring until the filter and ring sit on the rim of the container. Be gentle, so as not to tear the filter. If the filter tears, replace with a new one, then screw the cap on.

1. Mark each cigarette about 2 inches from the end, and place the other end into the holding tube. You will be "smoking" about 2 inches of each cigarette.

2. Light the cigarette with a match. Squeeze the aspirator bulb, and release it slowly. Every squeeze of the bulb equals one "puff" of a cigarette. Squeeze the bulb once every 30 seconds until you get down to the ink mark.

3. Remove the filter with forceps. Note the aroma and color of the filter. Compare this to the color comparison chart provided.

4. Repeat steps 1 through 4 for the remaining types: filtered regular and filtered "low tar."

Do the weights or colors of the filters differ?

_____

Which weighed the most?

_____

The least?

_____

What can you determine about unfiltered and filtered cigarettes from this experiment?

_____

_____

What can you determine about regular and low tar cigarettes from this experiment?

_____

_____

Procedure 2

Use one filtered regular cigarette and one filtered low tar cigarette of the same brand for this experiment.

1. Take one of each kind of cigarette. Remove the filter from one of them.

2. "Smoke" the cigarettes, as described in Procedure 1. Use a new filter disc for each cigarette. Remember to place a mark about 2 inches from the end of each cigarette.

3. Carefully remove the filter discs. Record which disc is darker.

4. Weigh each filter disc, or compare the filters to the color comparison chart to determine the amount of smoke collected by each.

5. Calculate the efficiency of the filters.

Example:

- Filter disc 1 (cigarette with removed filter) contains 60 milligrams (mg) of collected particles in smoke (tar).

- Filter disc 2 (cigarette with filter intact) contains 30 mg of collected particles. The quantity of particles collected by the filter tip is 60 mg - 30 mg = 30 mg

Use the following equation to determine the efficiency:

$$\frac{\text{Quantity of particles collected by the filter tip}}{\text{Quantity of particles collected by the filter disc \#1}} \;(X\ 100) = \text{Efficiency}$$

30 mg ÷ 60 mg (X 100) = 50%

This filter collected 50% of the smoke/particles, so 50% passed through the filter.

Did the filter disc trap the same amount of smoke as the cigarette filter? Calculate this by comparing the weight of the filter disc used with the removed filter cigarette to that of the cigarette filter that remained on the cigarette.

Which cigarette had the lowest smoke content?

Why don't cigarette companies manufacture a filter that traps 100% of the particles in smoke?

Supplemental Information

Alcohol

Slang Terms: beer, wine, liquor

Alcohol is a depressant to the central nervous system. It appears in the bloodstream within 5 minutes after ingestion, and reaches its highest blood-alcohol level in 30-60 minutes. Each ounce of alcohol consumed also kills about 10,000 more neurons than would normally die. This probably accounts for the mental deterioration seen in some alcoholics. Once it is absorbed into the bloodstream, it is rapidly distributed throughout the body, affecting almost every cell, organ, and level of functioning. Alcohol increases the workload of the heart, which in turn, can raise blood pressure and cause the heart to beat irregularly, which sometimes leads to heart failure. Heavy use of alcohol over time can damage the main heart muscles. Alcoholism is also the primary cause of liver disease and nutritional deficiencies. If a person abuses alcohol, they may become dependent upon it.

Use of alcohol during pregnancy may cause Fetal Alcohol Syndrome. A child born with Fetal Alcohol Syndrome can have the following defects: **Physical Defects:** abnormal facial features, growth deficiencies, low birth weight, heart defects, deformed joints, small head. **Mental Defects:** mental retardation, hyperactivity/restlessness, learning disabilities, behavior problems, poor coordination, delays in development.

Immediate Effects

loss of inhibitions/coordination	flushing and dizziness
impaired motor skills	slow reactions
blurred vision	slurred speech
sudden mood swings	vomiting
high blood pressure	irregular pulse
enlarged heart	unconsciousness
memory impairment	impairment of brain/nervous system functions

Long-term Effects

vitamin deficiencies

loss of muscle tissue

sexual impotence

lung disease

frequent infections

heart and blood disorders

cirrhosis of the liver

swelling of the liver

cancer

skin problems

inflammation of the pancreas

damage to the lining of stomach/small intestine

ulcers in the stomach/small intestine

tingling/loss of sensations in hands/feet

high risk for cancer

birth defects

inflamed liver (hepatitis)

brain damage

Psychological Effects

affects emotional reactions

impairs memory

alters moods

develops a false sense of confidence

Supplemental Information

Inhalants

Slang Terms: laughing gas, rush, whippets, poppers, and snappers

Inhalants are breathable chemicals that produce mind-altering vapors. People do not think of inhalants as drugs because most of the products were never meant to be used that way. Inhalants are ingested by "sniffing" or "snorting" (through the nose), "bagging" (inhaling fumes from a plastic bag), or "huffing" (stuffing an inhalant-soaked rag into the mouth). Nearly all inhalants produce effects similar to anesthetics, which act to slow down body functions; yet the user feels stimulated. Psychological effects occur rapidly because the substance travels directly to the brain after passing through the lungs and the left side of the heart.

When inhalants are used during pregnancy, the substances in solvents can pass through the placental barrier and enter the fetal bloodstream. However, except for evidence of birth defects among petrol inhalers, the evidence that use of other inhalants or solvents can damage the fetus is inconclusive.

Immediate Effects

nausea

bad breath

runny or bloody nose

feeling and looking tired

sneezing/coughing

chest pain

erratic heartbeat

loss of appetite

double vision

lack of coordination

eye irritation

vomiting, diarrhea

headache

ringing in ears

Long-term Effects

hand tremors

sores/rash around mouth/nose

weight loss

cardiac arrest

impaired respiratory system

death, asphyxiation/suffocation

less concern about appearance

fatigue, muscle fatigue

electrolyte (salt) imbalance

permanent damage to nervous system

impaired coordination/intelligence

brain/liver/kidney/blood/bone damage

Psychological Effects

anxiety, irritability/excitability

moody, restless activity

aggressive behavior

poor memory, confusion

lack of concentration

Four Classes of Inhalants

There are about 1,400 products potentially usable as inhalants.

1. Volatile solvents: gasoline, paint thinners, glue, cleaning solutions, etc.

2. Aerosols: spray paints, etc.

3. Anesthetic agents: chloroform, ether, oil, and grease dissolvers.

4. Amyl, butyl, and isobutyl nitrites: room fresheners.

Rohypnol

Slang Terms: roofies, ropies, ruffies, roche, la rocha, roachies, rope, R2, Mexican Valium

Rohypnol is a brand name for flunitrazepam, and is illegal in the United States. However, it is prescribed in more than 60 other countries to treat severe sleep disorders and serious psychiatric disorders. It is often taken with other drugs, such as heroin, cocaine, and alcohol. When taken with alcohol, Rohypnol produces disinhibition and amnesia, and it may become a gateway to harder drugs. Due to the effects of Rohypnol when combined with alcohol, it has been termed the "date rape drug". It has been reported that some men have used the Rohypnol/alcohol combination to drug women, causing them to black out, and creating a potential rape situation. Only 10 minutes after ingesting Rohypnol, a person may begin to feel dizzy, disoriented, too hot/too cold, and nauseated. The individual may have difficulty speaking, followed by passing out. Sedation occurs 20 to 30 minutes after administration of a 2-mg tablet, and lasts for approximately 8 hours. The individual will have no recollection of the events, that occurred while under the influence.

Immediate Effects

blackouts

sedation

drowsiness

disorientation

lack of inhibition

sense of aggressiveness

amnesia

muscle relaxation

dizziness

nausea

sense of fearlessness

Dependence

Physical and/or psychological dependence can occur. Physical dependence is characterized by withdrawal symptoms when Rohypnol use is suddenly discontinued.

Withdrawal Symptoms

headache/muscle pain	hallucinations
anxiety/tension	restlessness/irritability
confusion	convulsions/seizures (can occur weeks after last use)

Tranquilizers

Tranquilizers act as depressants to the central nervous system, and are used to calm, induce sleep, or decrease anxiety. They are prescribed medically to treat anxiety caused by stressors (such as insomnia and anxiety) in an individual's environment. The drugs are injected or swallowed in a pill form. Tranquilizers depress the effectiveness of the central nervous system, which, in turn, slows down the body. They also disrupt the psychomotor, intellectual, and perceptual functions, and can accumulate in body tissue after prolonged use. Dependence may occur from prescribed dosages. Tolerance and dependence can occur within 10 to 14 weeks of use. Large doses of tranquilizers are required by the user to maintain the feeling of well being. If tranquilizers are used for 4 to 6 weeks, then abruptly stopped, withdrawal symptoms are likely to occur. If tranquilizers are used in combination with other drugs, overdose or death can occur.

If used during pregnancy, they may cause congenital defects such as cleft lip, or cleft palate. Infants may experience withdrawal symptoms such as respiratory distress, feeding difficulties, disturbed sleeping patterns, decreased responsiveness, sweating, irritability, and fever. Some tranquilizers accumulate in higher concentrations in the bloodstream and organs of the infant than in the mother. They may also accumulate in higher concentrations in the breast milk than in the bloodstream.

There are two types of tranquilizers:

1. Major Tranquilizers: These tranquilizers are known as "antipsychotics", which are used for the treatment of mental illness.

2. Minor Tranquilizers: These tranquilizers decrease anxiety, as well as induce sleep. They also act as a general anesthetic, and cause dependence and tolerance.

Immediate Effects

The effects may appear rapidly and may last from hours to days.

reduced emotional reactions	reduced mental alertness
reduced attention span	sense of relaxation/well being
a "floating" sensation	depressed heartbeat and breathing
long periods of sleep	reduced feelings of anxiety
drowsiness	mental confusion
physical unsteadiness	

Long-term Effects

increased aggressiveness

withdrawal reactions

severe depression

physical dependence

increased tolerance

tolerance/dependence

Side Effects

skin rashes

dizziness

nausea

Withdrawal Symptoms

These symptoms can last from two to four weeks.

tremors

stomachaches

disturbed sleep

agitation

sweating

irritability

Barbituates

Slang Terms: barbs, red devils, goof balls, yellow jackets, block busters, pinks, reds and blues, Christmas trees

Physiological Symptoms: slurred speech, shallow breathing, sluggishness, fatigue, disorientation, lack of coordination, dilated pupils

Cathinone

The drug cathinone is found in the plant KHAT (*Catha edulis*), and is psychologically addictive.

It is commonly grown in Africa and southern Arabia, and used in social rituals. It is found in the form of dried leaves, crushed leaves, or powder. Cathinone acts as a stimulant to the central nervous system, similar to the effects of amphetamines. Other names for cathinone are qat, kat, chat, catha, quat, Abyssinian Tea, and African Tea.

Immediate Effects

increased blood pressure/respiration

thirst, after chewing KHAT

loquacity (increase in talking)

laughing

Psychological Effects

euphoria

paranoia

hallucinations

feelings of mental clarity

Methcathinone

Methcathinone is a synthetic, or man-made drug. Physical and/or psychological dependence may develop. Tolerance and withdrawal symptoms can occur after just one 6-10-day binge. This is a highly addictive drug, similar to crack cocaine, which is difficult to treat. Some of the chemicals in methcathinone are the same chemicals used in over-the-counter asthma and cold medicine, paint solvent, auto battery acid, Drano, and paint thinner. It is illegal in the United States, and has similar effects to amphetamines. Other names for methcathinone are cat, goob, Jeff, speed, bathtub speed, mulka, gagers/gaggers, The C, wild cat, wonder star, Cadillac express, ephedrone.

Immediate Effects

increased heart rate/respiration	dilated pupils
elevated body temperature	insomnia
tremors/muscle twitching	headaches
restlessness	convulsions

Psychological Effects

euphoria	increased alertness
hallucinations and delusions	paranoia/anxiety

Long-term Effects

paranoia	hallucinations
anxiety/depression	tremors/convulsions
anorexia/malnutrition	dehydration
stomach pain/nausea	nosebleeds/destruction of nasal tissue
elevated blood pressure	body aches
permanent brain damage	death

Amphetamines

Slang Terms: uppers, ups, wake ups, bennies, dexies, black beauties, jollies, speed

Amphetamines are drugs that is a stimulants to the central nervous system. They are colorless and may be inhaled, injected, or swallowed. These drugs may be used medically to treat depression, obesity, and other conditions. Nonmedically, they are used to avoid sleep, improve athletic performance, and counter the effects of depressant drugs.

It is possible for babies of mothers who use amphetamines to be born with cardiac defects, cleft palate, birth defects, addiction, and withdrawal. Amphetamines suppress appetite and give the user feelings of energy, so some people who use them to lose weight sometimes abuse them. Malnutrition can occur in the fetus because appetite is suppressed and/or decreased.

Immediate Effects

increased talkativeness	increased aggressiveness
increased breathing rate	increased heart rate
increased blood pressure	reduced appetite
dilated pupils	visual and auditory hallucinations

Effects of Large Doses

fever and sweating	dry mouth
headache	paleness
blurred vision	dizziness
irregular heartbeat	tremors
loss of coordination	collapse

Death may also occur due to burst blood vessels in the brain, heart failure, or very high fever.

Longterm Effects

violence/aggression	blockage of blood vessels
tolerance/dependence	addiction
infections from IV injections	malnutrition suppressed appetite
mental illness similar to	paranoid schizophrenia
increased susceptibility to illness	

Withdrawal Symptoms

severe exhaustion	deep sleep lasting from 24/48 hours
psychotic reaction	extreme hunger
deep depression	anxiety reactions
long, but disturbed, sleep	

Methamphetamine

Methamphetamines are synthetic amphetamines or stimulants that are produced and sold illegally in pill form, capsules, powder, and chunks. Two such Methamphetamines are crank and ice. Crank refers to any form of methamphetamine. Ice is a crystallized smokeable chunk form of methamphetamine that produces a more intense reaction than cocaine or speed. These drugs stimulate the central nervous system, and the effects may last anywhere from 8 to 24 hours. They are extremely addictive and produce a severe craving for the drug.

If methamphetamines are used during pregnancy, babies tend to be antisocial, incapable of bonding. They also suffer from tremors, birth defects, and are known to cry for up to 24 hours without stopping.

Short-term Effects

increased alertness	sense of well being
paranoia	intense high
hallucinations	aggressive behavior
increased heart rate	convulsions
violent behavior	insomnia
impaired speech	dry/itchy skin
loss of appetite	acne/sores
numbness	uncontrollable movements
high body temperature (> 108°, which can cause brain damage/death)	

Effects on the Mind

disturbed sleep

panic

moodiness/irritability

uninterested in friends/sex/food

severe depression

excessive excitation and talking

anxiousness/nervousness

false sense of confidence/power

aggressive/violent behavior

delusions of grandeur, leading to aggressive behavior

Long-term Effects

fatal kidney/lung disorders

depression

psychological problems

weight loss

malnutrition

liver damage

death

possible brain damage

hallucinations

violent/aggressive behavior

insomnia

lowered resistance to illnesses

stroke

behavior resembling paranoid schizophrenia

Cocaine

Slang Terms: coke, crack, dust, snow, blow

Cocaine is an addictive substance, which comes from coca leaves from the South American Coca plant, or is made synthetically. This drug acts as a stimulant to the central nervous system by blocking the reabsorbtion of dopamine (a chemical messenger that assists in normal functioning of the CNS, and is associated with pleasure and movement) in the brain. Cocaine appears as a white powder substance, which is inhaled, injected, freebased (smoked), or applied directly to the nasal membrane or gums. It gives the user a tremendous "rush" by using chemicals to trick the brain into feeling it has experienced pleasure. The effects of cocaine occur within the first few minutes, peak in 15-20 minutes, and disappear in about 1 hour. The immediate effects are what make cocaine so highly addicting, and each use of the drug can make the addiction stronger. The addiction can begin almost immediately after the first use.

Cocaine use during pregnancy can increase incidences of miscarriage, premature labor, kidney and respiratory ailments, and Sudden Infant Death Syndrome. Fetal addiction may occur before birth, as well as prenatal strokes due to fluctuations in blood pressure. In males, cocaine may attach to the sperm, causing damage to the cells of the fetus. After birth, the baby may suffer from withdrawl symptoms.

Psychological Effects

increased heart rate/breathing

weight loss

insomnia

pallor (paleness)

dilated pupils

fatigue

headaches

seizures

nausea

tremors

rapid breathing

impotence

cold sweats

constipation

blurred vision

nasal congestion

Health Problems

ulceration of nasal membrane

respiratory arrest

lung damage

cardiac arrest

physiological seizures

Withdrawal Symptoms

extreme irritability

nausea

sluggishness

unorganized thinking

Crack

Crack is chemically altered cocaine, and found as small, hard, white chunks. It is a stimulant to the central nervous system, and is deadlier than other forms of cocaine. Crack is extremely addictive. Anyone using crack can become an addict in 2 to 3 weeks, and in some cases, people who try crack become instantly addicted the first time they use the drug. It reaches the brain in less than 8 seconds, and produces a "high" that peaks in 10-15 seconds and lasts only 15 minutes. This "high" is produced because crack tricks the brain into releasing chemicals that produce a false feeling of intense pleasure.

Crack use during pregnancy can cause increased incidence of stillbirths, miscarriages, and premature (often fatal) labor and delivery. In males, the cocaine in crack may attach to the sperm, causing damage to the cells of the fetus. Babies exposed to cocaine experience painful and life- threatening withdrawal. They are irritable and have decreased ability to regulate body temperature and blood sugar, which puts them at an increased risk of having seizures.

Physical Effects

chronic sore throat

shortness of breath

lung cancer

lung damage

weight loss

increased blood pressure

brain seizures

sweating

stroke

death

hoarseness

bronchitis

emphysema

burning of lips, tongue, throat

slowed digestion

vessel constriction

increased heart rate

dilated pupils

heart attack

respiratory problems

increased blood sugar levels/body temperature

suppressed desire for food, sex, friends, family, social contacts

Emotional/Psychological Effects

sadness and depression

sleeplessness

intense craving of the drug

delusions/hallucinations

loss of interest in appearance

extreme paranoia

schizophrenic-like psychosis

Crack Addiction

There are four stages that have been identified with crack addiction:

intense feeling of stimulation

irritability, sleeplessness and paranoia

followed by feelings of sadness and depression

schizophrenic-like psychosis with delusions and hallucinations

Withdrawal Symptoms

nausea

intense craving of the drug

paranoia

physical problems

Marijuana

Slang Terms: pot, grass, weed, mj, reefer, joint, Columbian

Marijuana is obtained from the hemp plant and is smoked in cigarettes or pipes or is eaten. Marijuana comes from the plant Cannabis sativa. The psychoactive (mind-altering) ingredient in marijuana is THC (delta-9-tetrahydrocannabinol) this is stored in the fat of the body, and can cause harm to the brain and body by causing the cells to become toxic up to 30 days after the last use. The amount of THC determines how strong the effects will be. Smoking marijuana will cause immediate physical effects, such as an increased heart rate and pulse rate. It increases the heart rate by as much as 50%, depending on the content of THC. As use of marijuana increases, the tolerance level increases, and as a result, dependence is more likely. The marijuana user may experience a physical dependence on the drug because <u>marijuana cigarettes contain more of the known carcinogen benzopyrene than tobacco cigarettes</u>. Psychological addiction to marijuana causes the strongest dependence and can occur over a very short time period. The effects of marijuana on the brain are very similar to the effects of aging. This places the long time user at high risk for serious and premature memory disorders. Marijuana use also causes amotivational syndrome, meaning that the user will lose interest in activities and lose drive and motivation.

Marijuana smoking has been proven to have adverse effects on the female reproductive system, as well as the health of the child. Use during pregnancy has been associated with diminished birth weight and the presence of physical and mental characteristics similar to fetal alcohol syndrome (facial deformities, heart defects, deformed joints, low birth weight, small head). Marijuana has also been found to cause tremors and startle response withdrawal symptoms in newborn children.

Immediate Effects

increased pulse rate

loss of logical thinking

restlessness

hallucinations

psychotic episodes

impaired motor ability

altered perception

impaired ability, to concentrate/learn

short-term memoryloss

confusion

excitement

anxiety or panic

impaired coordination

increased appetite

impaired driving ability

Long-term Effects

toxic effect on brain nerve cells

risk of chronic bronchitis

energy loss

memory impairment

suppressed effects on sperm

blood vessel blockage

increased risk of lung cancer

respiratory diseases/cancer

slow, confused thinking

apathy

impaired immune system

Nicotine

Nicotine is a substance found in tobacco, and is found in all tobacco products, such as cigarettes, pipe tobacco, chewing tobacco, and cigars. When a person smokes a tobacco product, they inhale the smoke, which contains nicotine, as well as more than 500 chemicals. This is the drug in tobacco that causes addiction. The smoke from tobacco also contains tar, which is damaging to the mouth, throat, and lungs. It reaches the brain within 10 seconds after intake, and is a stimulant to the brain and the central nervous system.

Women who smoke have a greater risk of premature detachment of the placenta. Once detachment has occurred, perinatal death rates also increase. This risk increases by 20% with every 1/2 pack of cigarettes smoked. Women who smoke also suffer from more reproductive tract infections, fertility and menstrual disorders, earlier menopause, and problems during pregnancy. Babies of mothers who smoke can suffer from low birth weight, premature birth, as well as impaired mental and physical development. There is also a greater occurrence of miscarriage and stillbirths, as well as Sudden Infant Death Syndrome (SIDS). These babies will also have a greater likelihood of being hyperactive.

Immediate Effects

increased blood pressure

thickening of blood

decreased skin temperature

stimulation of the CNS

diarrhea

increased heart rate

narrowing of arteries

increased respiration

vomiting

Long-term Effects

high blood pressure

depletion of vitamin C

cancer of mouth, throat, lungs

bronchitis and/or emphysema

weight loss

abnormal sperm in males

blockage of blood vessels

reduced immune system

cancer of respiratory tract

stomach ulcers

dryness/wrinkling of the skin

Withdrawal Symptoms

drop in pulse rate	drop in blood pressure
disturbance of sleep	slower reactions
tension	restlessness
depression	irritability
constipation	difficulty concentrating
craving for tobacco	

Anabolic Steroids

Anabolic steroids are a form of the synthetic male hormone, testosterone, which is often used to increase muscle size and strength. They are found in liquid or pill form, and are medically used to increase body tissue.

Side Effects

Cardiovascular System:

cholesterol modifications	heart disease
anaphylactic shock	high blood pressure
death	

Reproductive System:

genital atrophy	genital swelling
sexual dysfunction	sterility
impotence	prostate enlargement
menstrual irregularities	

Psychological Symptoms:

depression	listlessness
aggressive/combative behavior	violence, paranoia/mood swings
manic episodes	hallucinations

Liver:

cancer	tumors
hepatitis	

Other Side Effects of Steroids

acne	hairiness in women
male-pattern baldness	oily skin
stunted growth	abdominal/stomach pains
diarrhea	changes in bowel/urinary habits
gallstones	hives
headaches (continuous)	excessive calcium
insomnia	kidney stones/disease
muscle cramps	nausea/vomiting
purple, red spots on or in body	rash

Other Side Effects of Steroids (continued)

sore throat

unexplained weight loss

unusual bleeding

unusual weight gain

breath odor (continuous)

yellowing of eyes/skin

Hallucinogens

Slang Terms: magic mushrooms, LSD, acid, windowpane, microdots, purple haze

Hallucinogens can be man made, or grown naturally. They have no taste and are found as tablets, capsules, tiny sheets of paper, or liquid. Certain types of mushrooms and datura plants are also hallucinogens. These drugs are injected, taken orally, or eaten. Hallucinogens produce radical changes in the mental state, involving distortions of reality and acute hallucinations. They also affect the way a person experiences his/her sense of taste, smell, hearing, and vision. They have no prescribed medical use, and are only made and sold illegally. With large doses, the hallucinations can be frightening and disturbing. Tolerance may occur rapidly from the use of hallucinogens, and can also cause cross-tolerance. This means that the use of one hallucinogen causes and increases tolerance to other hallucinogens. A dependence on hallucinogens is likely, but no withdrawal symptoms occur when use of the drug is discontinued.

Hallucinogens radically affect the brain, thus affecting the personality. Serious mental illness may occur. Unpleasant episodes (or "bad trips") may cause psychological damage and lead to suicide. They may affect the same user in man, different ways during the same "trip". The effects of a "trip" may be experienced 15-30 minutes after use, and the effects may last up to 24 hours. A person may re-experience effects of a "trip", days, weeks, or years after use of the drug. This phenomenon is called a "flashback". Some people may remain permanently brain-damaged or psychotic from the drugs, and this condition cannot be reversed. The use of hallucinogens during pregnancy can increase the risk of spontaneous abortions, as well as congenital and chromosome damage.

Immediate Effects

mood modifying

hallucination

panic/loss of control

emotional instability

increased blood pressure

raised body temperature

suicidal tendencies

anxiety

changes in perception

intense awareness

unpredictable behavior

violent behavior

increased heart rate

dilated pupils

tremors

Long-term Effects

brain damage

depression

impaired memory

mental confusion

psychological dependence

death

chromosome damage

psychiatric complication

poor attention span

toxic level of tolerance

suicide

Ecstasy

Slang Terms: wonder drug, XTC, X

Ecstasy is an illegal synthetic or designer drug. Designer drugs are drugs that mimic an already illegal drug by slightly altering the chemical composition. Ecstasy is also called MDMA, which stands for methylenedioxymethamphetamine. The amount of MDMA needed to get "high" is close to the toxic dose. Ecstasy is similar to methamphetamine or MDA, which is another designer drug, in its chemistry; therefore, it may have similar effects to other amphetamines and acts as a stimulant to the central nervous system. Ecstasy can deplete as much as 90% of the brain's serotonin supply with two weeks of use. Serotonin is a neurotransmitter in the brain, which controls activities such as regulating aggression, thinking, sleeping, eating, sensitivity to pain, and mood.

Immediate Effects

feelings of detachment

muscle tension

sweating or chills

tremors

increased heart rate

dehydration

loss of hunger, sleep, sexual arousal

rapid eye movement

insomnia

hypertension

decreased appetite

death

Long-term Effects

anorexia

kidney failure

change in emotion

change in brain chemicals

high blood pressure

stroke

memory loss

Psychological Effects

confusion

sleep problems

paranoia

panic

depression

anxiety

hallucinations

psychotic episodes

Herbal Ecstasy

The main drug in herbal ecstasy is ephedra or ma huang, a natural herb. It is legal in most states; although some states have recently banned the drug. Ephedra has been used for weight control, upper respiratory treatment, and as an energy booster. Other brand names of drugs containing ingredients similar to herbal ecstasy are Cloud 9, Ultimate Xphoria, X, and Rave Energy.

Effects

liver failure	increased blood pressure
increased heart rate	palpitations
stroke	fainting
euphoric feeling	increased awareness
seizures	heart attacks
death	

PCP

Slang Terms: angel dust, angel hair, mist, flying saucers, hog

Usual Form: white powder and tablets

How Taken:

swallowed	sniffed
smoked	injected

Psychological Symptoms

nausea	vomiting
double vision	sweating/flushing
increased heart rate	anxiety
panic	numbness
hallucinations	

Opiates (Narcotics)

Slang Terms:

- Codeine: schoolboy

- Heroin: H, stuff, junk, horse, Harry, smack, Demerol

- Morphine: M, white stuff, cube, morf, mud

Opiates are habit-forming drugs that dull the senses, relieve pain, and induce sleep. Some forms of opiates are morphine, heroin, and codeine. A tolerance to the drugs may occur if a person uses them over a period of time; cross tolerance may also occur. This means that if a person uses one type of opiate, they will develop a tolerance to all opiates. Addiction to opiates such as heroin causes many dangerous physical and psychological effects. Withdrawal symptoms begin within 24 hours after the last use, and may last up to 7-10 days.

Research has shown that nearly half of the women who are dependent on opiates during pregnancy and childbirth suffer anemia, heart disease, diabetes, pneumonia, or hepatitis. These women also experience more spontaneous abortions, breech deliveries, caesarean sections, premature births, stillbirths, and infants with withdrawal symptoms. Many of these babies die.

Immediate Effects

decreased awareness of the outside world

vomiting

drowsiness

nodding off

depression of respiration

unconsciousness

dilated pupils

Effects of Prolonged Use

physical dependence

psychological dependence

reduced bowel movements

infections of heart lining/valve

skin abscesses

lethargy/indifference to environment/people

congested lungs

death

With Large Doses

user cannot be awakened

pupils become very small

breathing slows down

death from overdose

skin becomes cold/moist/bluish in color

Withdrawal Symptoms

uneasiness

yawning

tremors

crying

diarrhea

weight loss

abdominal cramps

goose bumps

runny nose

severe craving for the drug

Questions

1. From the supplemental information, list four examples of stimulants to the Central Nervous System.

   _____

   _____

   _____

2. From the supplemental information, list four examples of depressants to the Central Nervous System.

   _____

   _____

3. Which drug contains THC, and what does THC stand for?

   _____

   _____

4. Which drug is also known as the "Date Rape Drug"?

_____

5. What is cross-tolerance? Give two examples of drugs that are associated with this condition.

_____

_____

_____

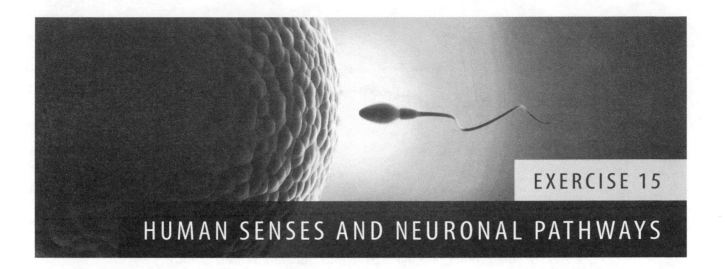

HUMAN SENSES AND NEURONAL PATHWAYS

Objectives

The objectives of this exercise are to understand the physiology behind vision and certain visual disorders; to understand how hearing works in humans and to detect possible hearing disorders; to grasp the concept of mechanoreception, photoreception, and acoustical reception.

INTRODUCTION

Our senses are divided into two categories: **somatic sensations**, which include touch, pressure, temperature, and pain; and **special senses**, which include taste, smell, hearing, and vision. All senses are accessed via the **sensory system** of the central nervous system. Sensory cells detect stimuli from external and internal environments and transmit signals to the nervous system.

Our nerve cells have three parts: the **cell body**, an **axon**, and **dendrites** (**Fig. 1**). Dendrites receive signals coming to the nerve cell body; axons carry that signal from the nerve cell body. Nerve cells are particularly sensitive to chemical changes. When a stimulus is reached by the dendrites, which is then passed on to the axon, the membrane of the nerve cell opens protein channels, or gates, allowing sodium found in abundance **outside** the cell to rush in. Once there is more sodium inside the cell than outside the cell, the sodium channels close. This causes the channels for potassium flow to open. Since there is more potassium found **inside** the cell, potassium rushes out of the cell (remember diffusion?). As the sodium/potassium gates open and close in one part of the membrane, they cause the same thing to happen in an adjacent part of the membrane. This sequence of events continues along the length of the axon, thus allowing the conduction of the signal.

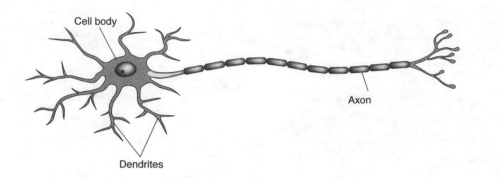

Figure 1: A neuron.

In this continuation of your project, you will explore three different senses: vision, or **photoreception**; hearing, or **acoustical reception**; and touch, or **mechanoreception**. Each of the organs involved in these senses has a circuit of nerves that run impulses from that organ to the brain. Once the stimulus reaches the brain, the nervous system is able to distinguish between different stimuli based on the part of the brain that receives the signal. It doesn't matter *what* the stimulus is, but it does matter *where* the impulse goes.

Part I - Vision

Vision, also referred to as **photoreception**, occurs when light rays meet at the back of the eye and stimulate the retina. The **optic nerve** then transmits a signal to the brain, which decodes the signal and allows us to recognize the pattern.

The retina is made up of **photoreceptors** called **rods** and **cones**. Rods detect very dim light, and cones detect bright light and color. It is the presence of cones within the retina of an organism that determines if it sees in color or in monochrome.

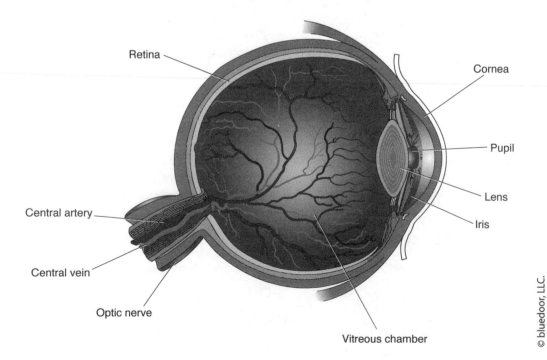

Figure 2: Anatomy of the human eye.

Procedure 1

Detecting Eye Dominance

Our eyes, just like our hands, show right-left dominance. Eye dominance can determine how we do certain tasks, such as hitting a baseball.

1. Take a piece of notebook paper and roll it length-wise into a loose tube.

2. Hold the tube straight out in front of you as far as you can. Using both eyes, look through the tube at a fixed object in the room.

3. Without moving the tube, close your left eye.

Did the object stay in place, or did it appear to move?

4. Now close the other eye.

Again, did the object stay in place or did it appear to move?

If the object did not move with either eye, you are central-eye dominant. If the object moved while closing your right eye, you are left-eye dominant. If it moved while closing your left eye, you are right-eye dominant.

How do you think eye dominance would affect your driving if you were unable to use one of your eyes?

You wouldn't see the road as well

Procedure 2

Determining Your Near Point

Are you able to clearly see objects that are up close? If so, how close? The distance between an object and your eye, when an object is sharply in focus, is called the near point. For people who are farsighted or hypermetropic, close objects are often blurred or indistinguishable; their near point is much further away than individuals with perfect vision or those who are nearsighted. Interestingly, a natural consequence of aging is that the near point for most people gets farther away.

1. If you wear glasses or contact lenses, keep them on.

2. Hold this page in front of you at arm's length. Choose one word on the page, close your left eye and focus on that word.

3. Move the page closer until the word gets blurry. Move it back until it is back in focus.

4. When the word is back in focus, have your partner measure the distance between your eye and the page in centimeters.

5. Repeat with your right eye closed.

Near point for right eye: _____4_____ cm   Near point for left eye: _____6_____ cm

Is your vision the same in both eyes? _No, my right eye gets clear_

How do glasses or contact lenses change your vision? _they adjust_
the distance it appears to be

Procedure 3

Astigmatism

The cornea of your eye acts as a fixed lens that lets light into the eye. If this lens is unevenly curved, it prevents your eye from bending incoming light rays to the same focal point. People with astigmatism generally have difficulty seeing at night. Your instructor has an astigmatism test chart. Face the chart and stand 24-30 inches away. If you wear glasses, take them off. Cover one eye and stare at the center of the chart. If all of the lines coming from the circle are of an even width and color, you do not have astigmatism. If any of the lines seem thicker or darker than others, you most likely have astigmatism. Repeat with the other eye. If you wear glasses, put them back on to see if they correct for astigmatism.

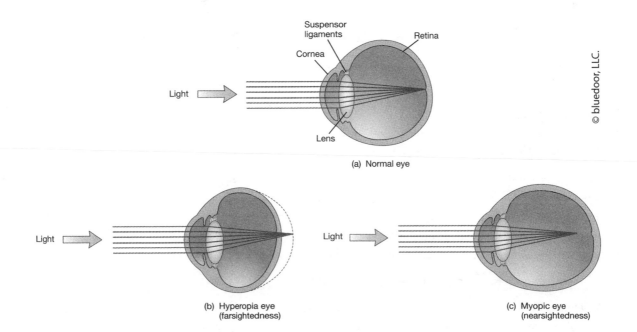

© bluedoor, LLC.

Figure 3: Nearsightedness, farsightedness, and normal vision in humans.

Procedure 4

Color Blindness

Color blindness is usually inherited and is a sex-linked characteristic most commonly found in males. Red-green color blindness is the most common, and occurs when there is a lack of red- and green-sensitive cones. Yellow-blue color blindness is rare (red cones are present, but not green), and complete color blindness is even more rare (no cones are present).

Use either the Psuedo-Isochromatic plates or the Ishihara test book provided by your lab instructor to test for color blindness. If using the Ishihara test book, plate numbers 11 and 15 do not have numbers; indicate what color(s) you can trace in the figure. Go to a window or an area with bright, natural light. Hold the plates about 60 cm from your partner's face, and ask your partner to tell you the number in the mosaic. Make sure you do not point to the number or in any way indicate the location of the number. Have your partner test your color vision. Record your responses in Table 1.

Was your partner able to detect all colors? _YM_ Were you? _yy_

Table 1: Responses to color vision test plate.

Plate Number	Subject's Response
1	ah men
2	
3	
4	
5	
6	
7	
8	
9	
10	
11	
12	
13	
14	

If you both could detect colors, did it take longer for one of you to identify the number in the mosaic? If so, what do you think this can tell you about individual color perception?

No, we were the same

The correct interpretations for the color blindness test charts are listed in **Tables 3 and 4** at the end of the lab exercise.

Procedure 5

Field of Vision

Field of vision refers to the angles at which you can detect an object (total field of vision) and the angle at which you can read a letter (reading field of vision).

For this simple test, you will be using vision disk tests. Your instructor will show you how to use the disks, and you will be working in pairs, taking turns being the "subject" and the "tester".

© bluedoor, LLC.

To find out the total field of vision and your total reading field of vision, add up the right and left measurements. For the field of vision, this represents the angle at which you are able to perceive an object, and for the reading field of vision the angle or range within which you are able to read.

Record your results in the following table:

1. Right side field of vision: _____ 76 _____
2. Right side reading field of vision: 105 _____
3. Left side field of vision: 116 _____
4. Left side reading field of vision: 61 _____

Total Field of Vision (add 1 and 3): _____ 215 ____

Total Reading Field of Vision (add 2 and 4): ___ 137 ___

Procedure 6

Visual Acuity

Visual acuity, or sharpness of vision, is generally tested with a Snellen eye chart. This test is based on the fact that letters of a certain size can be seen clearly by eyes with normal vision at a specific distance. The distance at which a normal eye can read each group of letters is printed at the end of each line.

To test for visual acuity, you will find a Snellen eye chart posted on one of the lab walls. A line will be marked on the floor that will correspond to a distance of 20 feet, or 6 meters, from the chart.

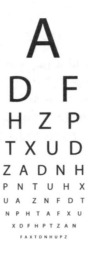

To proceed with the test, have your partner stand at the line and cover one eye with his or her hand. As the person reads each consecutive line, check for accuracy. If the individual wears glasses, do the test twice, once without glasses, and once with glasses. It's not necessary to do this with contact lenses, but make a note that they were in place.

Record the number of the line that corresponds to the smallest size of letters read.

What the numbers mean:

- If it is 20/20, the person's vision for that eye is normal.

- If it is 20/40, or another ratio with a value less than one, the person has less than normal vision. For example, a person with 20/40 vision needs to get as close as 20 feet to read something that a person with normal vision can read at 40 feet.

- If the result was 20/15 or a ratio with a value more than one, the person has better than normal vision. It means he or she can stand at 20 feet from the chart and read letters that can be read by a person with normal vision at 15 feet.

After recording the results for the first eye, repeat the process for the other eye. *Make a note when glasses or contact lenses were used.*

Visual Acuity Results:

Right Eye: _____ 20 20 _____

Left Eye: _____ 20 20 _____

Part II - Hearing

Hearing occurs with the aid of **acoustical receptors**, a type of mechanoreceptor that responds to vibrations. In vertebrates, these receptors are in the form of **hair cells**, which bend due to direct or indirect vibrations. These specialized hair cells transmit signals to the brain via the **auditory nerve**. The brain then processes the information and may be able to determine the source and type of sound that created the stimulus.

Hearing Loss

There are two types of hearing loss: **sensorineural**, or nerve deafness, and **conductive** loss. Sensorineural loss occurs when the sound receptors or the neurons that transmit impulses to the brain are damaged. Aging or prolonged exposure to loud noises can cause sensorineural loss, and it is usually permanent. Loss of conduction occurs when sound vibrations cannot reach the inner ear. This type of hearing loss can sometimes be corrected with hearing aids or through surgery.

In this exercise, you will conduct a test to detect hearing loss, and differentiate between conduction loss and sensorineural loss.

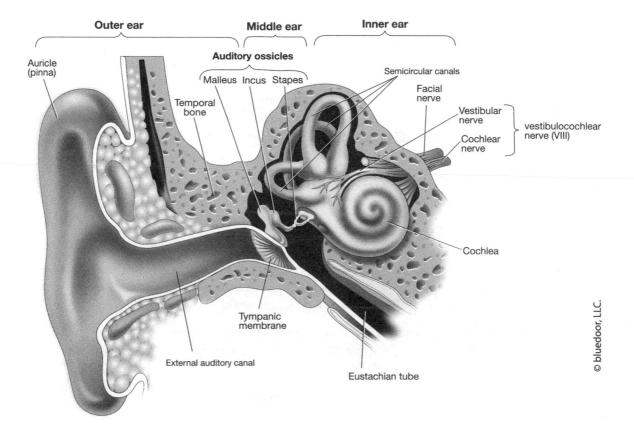

Figure 4: Anatomy of the human ear.

Procedure 7

Work in pairs. Have your partner sit and plug his/her left ear with cotton. Strike a tuning fork against the heel of your hand, but do not strike it against a hard object. Immediately hold the end of the tuning fork against the right mastoid process (bone behind the ear.) Record the amount of time that your partner can actually hear the tuning fork. When the sound can no longer be heard, strike the tuning fork again, and place the fork 1 inch from the right ear. Record the amount of time that your partner can hear the tuning fork. Repeat the procedure on the left side. Lab partners should change duties and repeat the procedure.

Times for right ear:

Mastoid process ___10___

1 in. from ear ___5___

Times for left ear:

Mastoid process ___10___

1 in. from ear ___5___

In subjects with normal hearing, the tuning fork should be heard twice as long by air (1 in. from ear) as by bone (against the mastoid process). If bone conduction is longer, the subject may have conductive hearing loss. If the subject does not hear the tuning fork, or hears the tuning fork very briefly, he/she may have more severe sensorineural hearing loss.

After attending a concert, many people experience a temporary reduction in hearing. What kind of loss are they experiencing, and why does it occur?

_____sensorineural, the sound receptors_____

_____or neurons are damaged_____

_____

Briefly explain the way sound is perceived by individuals in the space below:

_____hairs vibrate which sends_____

_____signals to the brain_____

_____

_____

Part III - Distribution of Touch Receptors

Sensations that fall under the somatic category are broken down into **mechanoreceptors, pain receptors, thermo receptors**, and **electromagnetic receptors**. Mechanoreceptors are located both near the surface of our skin and imbedded deeply in our skin. They are found throughout the body, and are more abundant in some regions compared to others. Those receptors lying closer to the surface of our skin detect light touch or pressure; those more deeply imbedded detect strong touch or pressure. Pain receptors are also located in the epidermis of the skin and are grouped according to the stimulus, such as excess heat, pressure, or chemicals released from inflamed tissue. Thermo receptors are thought to be located in the skin, and respond to heat and cold in order to regulate body temperature. Finally, electromagnetic receptors respond to electromagnetic energy such as visible light, electricity, and magnetism.

In order to discern the difference between one touch or pressure stimulus and another, each stimuli must invoke an action potential of a separate touch receptor. Action potentials allow the transmission of the nerve signal. Some action potentials are generated only at the beginning of the stimulus and at the end of the stimulus (such as those caused by tickling); many others are generated as long as the stimulus is applied, allowing you to sense touch as it is happening.

What regions of the body do you think have the greatest abundance of touch receptors? Why? Where are the least? Why?

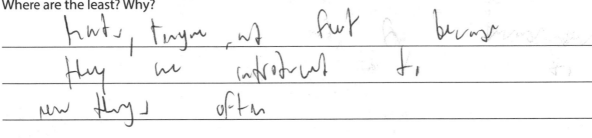

Procedure 8

1. Have your lab partner close his/her eyes. Touch the skin of the inside of his or her forearm with one or two points of a pair of scissors spread far apart. Have your partner tell you if he or she feels one tip or two. Make sure you alternate the number of tips you touch to the skin.

2. Reduce the distance between the scissors tips and continue touching your partner's forearm, alternating the number of tips used.

3. When your partner feels only one tip 75% of the time, even though you are using two tips, stop and measure the distance (in cm) between the tips of the scissors. This is the minimum distance needed to produce a two-point sensation.

Table 2: The minimum distance required for a two-point sensation at various parts of the body.

Location of body	Distance (cm) of scissor points
Inside of forearm	12
Back of neck	18
Palm of hand	18
Tip of index finger	2

4. Repeat this exercise on the back of the neck, the palm of the hand, and the tip of the index finger. Record the distances in **Table 2**.

Which part of your body is most sensitive to touch? _____ finger _____

Which part of your body is least sensitive? _____ neck _____ or _____ hand _____

Do your results agree with what you predicted before beginning the exercise? Why or why not?

_____ yes _____

_____

_____

_____

Now explore how intensity plays a role in sensation, by using different temperatures to invoke a response.

1. Fill three large beakers or basins: one with ice water, one with warm water, and one with water at room temperature.

2. Place your index finger in each pan, beginning with the ice water, then the warm water, and finally the room-temperature water. Were you able to detect the differences in temperature?

_____ yes _____

_____

3. Now fill the pans with water containing only slight differences in temperature. How does this affect your ability to detect temperature differences? Are you able to detect the differences as well? Why or why not?

_____ No, it makes it a little harder _____

_____

_____

_____

4. Now place your right hand in ice water and your left hand in warm water. Let your hands acclimate to the water temperatures. Can you still detect a temperature difference? Why or why not?

yes, cause you can

What do you think temperature receptors really respond to?

if the water temperature
is rising

Part IV: Smell and Taste

Smell and taste are related in that both senses are activated by external chemoreceptors. These are receptor cells that are triggered by chemical signals (odor molecules or different tastes). In mammals, taste receptors are located in **taste buds**, most of which are on the surface of the tongue. Each taste receptor responds to a wide array of chemicals. It is the pattern of taste receptor response that determines perceived flavor. In mammals, olfactory receptors line the upper portion of the nasal cavity. The binding of odor molecules to olfactory receptors initiates signal-transduction pathways that conduct the signal to the brain.

Smell: Olfactory Sense

What is smell? Smell, or **olfaction**, is the detection of different molecules by receptors in the nose. The molecules we can detect have to have some "olfactory properties" (basically, smell!). Among other properties, they have to be water soluble, and have some fat solubility, surface activity, and a certain molecular weight. The actual region in our nasal passages that is in charge of smelling is only about 2.5 cm square, but contains about 50 million receptor cells.

This region contains the olfactory epithelium: a layer of olfactory neurons that extends into our mucous surface by means of cilia. The mucous traps the odor molecules and dissolves them. The cilia are part of the olfactory neurons that transport the signal into the brain. The olfactory receptor neurons turnover rate is approximately 40 days.

Fact: These olfactory neurons were the first neurons known to be able to regenerate.

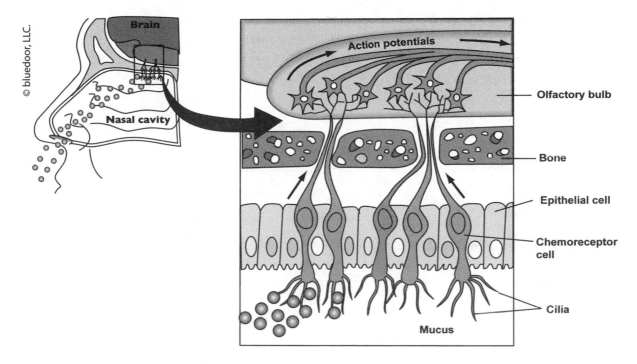

Measuring Olfactory Fatigue

Olfactory fatigue is a property of smell in which the ability to detect an odor decreases with continued exposure to that odor.

In this exercise, you will be measuring your olfactory fatigue for different substances. At the same time, write down what you think the unknown substance is. Compare your notes with the rest of the class, and your unknowns with your teacher.

Need:

- Film canister containers w/holes on lid
- Odorants
- Timer/stopwatch
- Water

Procedure 9

Work in pairs. Hold the containers about 15 inches from your nose. Wave your hand to produce a constant fanning of the smell into your nose. Make sure you breathe normally and DO NOT hyperventilate. Your partner will mark the time you start smelling the odor, and continue keeping track of the time until you cannot smell it anymore. Write down this time. Repeat with the other 4 substances.

Odor Fatigue Substance 1: _____2_____ Time: _____6_____

Odor Fatigue Substance 2: _____5_____ Time: _____9_____

Odor Fatigue Substance 3: _____9_____ Time: _____7_____

Odor Fatigue Substance 4: _____1_____ Time: _____5_____

Odor Fatigue Substance 5: _____5_____ Time: _____6_____

Did the time vary between substances? If so, can you think of any reasons?

_____yes, if its a stronger smell_____

_____

_____

Did you know that just as some people cannot see or hear, other people cannot smell? This condition is called **anosmia**. Can you think of any serious problems an anosmic person could have?

_____not being able to smell if_____

_____there is fire_____

Taste: Gustatory Sense

The **gustatory** sense is mediated by *taste buds*, small onion-shaped bags on the papillae of the tongue and elsewhere that contain 50 to 75 sensitive cells each. Liquids can pass through a small pore to reach the sensitive cells. Remarkably, the taste-sensitive cells have a limited lifetime, and are constantly being replaced.

Humans not only have taste buds on the surface of the tongue, but also on the lips (especially salt-sensitive ones), the inside of the cheeks, the underside of the tongue, the roof of the mouth, and the back of the throat.

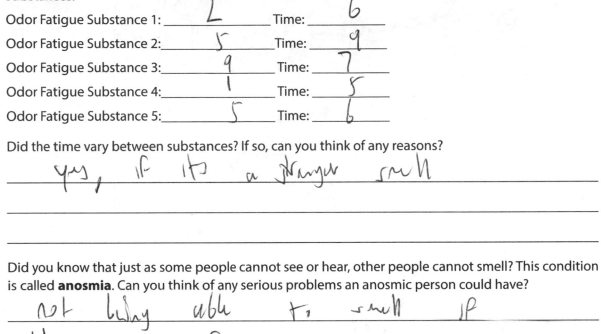

Taste bud containing taste-sensitive cells

Tongue areas

© bluedoor, LLC.

Procedure 10

In this lab, you will be trying to figure out what areas of the tongue can detect different tastes, and if there is any relation between taste and smell.

Materials:

- Toothpicks

- Flavors: bitter, sour, salty, and sweet

- Water to rinse mouth between flavors

- Paper cups

Pour a small amount of an unknown substance into a paper cup. Lick a toothpick and dip it into the flavored powder. Test one flavor at a time in each area of the tongue and label with A, B, C, or D in the tongue diagram where you tasted the flavor. Repeat with all four unknown substances.

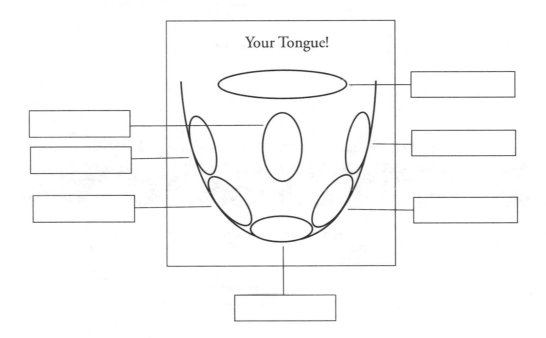

What were the unknown substances?

A. _____   B. _____

C. _____   D. _____

Table 3: Correct numbers for the Pseudo-isochromatic plates for testing color perception.

Plate Number	Correct # – Pseudo-isochromatic
1	12
2	6
3	42
4	56
5	57
6	75
7	5
8	3
9	56
10	27
11	89
12	86
13	15
14	74
15	47

Table 4: Correct numbers for Ishihara's test for color deficiency; x denotes cannot detect.

Plate Number	Normal vision	Rred-green deficiencies	Total color blindness
1	12	12	12
2	8	3	x
3	5	2	x
4	29	70	x
5	74	21	x
6	7	x	x
7	45	x	x
8	2	x	x
9	x	x	x
10	16	x	x
11	traceable	x	x
12	35	5 or 3	x
13	96	6 or 9	x
14	Can trace 2 lines	Trace either purple or red	x

References:

Olfaction. John C. Leffingwell, Ph.D., Leffingwell & Associates
http://md1.csa.com/crw/web/web-smell.html

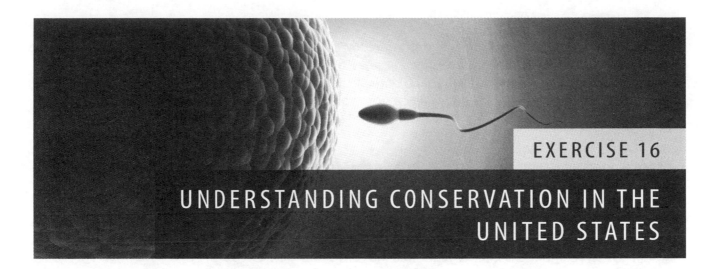

UNDERSTANDING CONSERVATION IN THE UNITED STATES

Objectives

In this lab, you will learn to understand what "conservation" means and how it is applied to various environmental concerns. Specifically, you will examine the importance of wetland conservation, water conservation, and critical species conservation. You will learn about the functional values of wetlands and observe historical wetland losses in the United States through map analysis. To understand water conservation, you will analyze water quality parameters by testing water samples to identify differences between natural and municipal water supplies. Map analysis will be used to understand what happens to water quality in a stream as it passes through several natural and man-made areas. Finally, you will examine how critical species are listed for protection in the United States, and you will role play a scenario to understand various viewpoints in critical species conservation.

INTRODUCTION

Understanding Conservation

Conservation is the controlled use and systematic protection of natural resources. Conservation practices include preserving land areas and regulating activities within them. For example, national parks are designated to preserve ecologically important areas. When you travel to these parks, you must follow regulations that prohibit you from collecting plants and animals. In another example, wetlands are protected in the United States through regulations aimed at limiting human development in these habitats. Conservation practices can be implemented in a variety of areas, such as upland forests and prairies, or aquatic areas, such as lakes and wetlands.

Conservation is a very broad topic and does not just encompass preservation of land, as illustrated by the above examples. Conservation practices include regulations to protect individual species that may be in danger of extinction. Other practices may involve removal of **exotic species** to maintain and enhance the survival of native communities of plants and animals. Conservation practices also include such things as energy conservation and water conservation.

Although conservation includes a wide array of topics, this lab will focus on three distinct themes. You will examine the important, and sometimes controversial, aspects of conservation as they pertain to **wetlands**, **water quality**, and **critical species**, and you will gain an understanding of how this topic affects your life and the decisions you make.

Wetlands

The colonists who explored the United States in the 1700s and 1800s viewed wetlands as dark, dismal places, teaming with vectors carrying malaria and yellow fever. Colonists were eager to drain these wetlands and convert them to upland for urban settlement and agriculture. Since the 1600s, Americans have converted more than half the wetland resources in this country to dry land. However, as these transformations took place, people began to notice the functional values these wetlands served. In the last thirty years, wetland conversion has slowed significantly. Attempts are now being made to restore degraded wetlands, such as the Florida Everglades. Wetlands are now protected such that land owners or businesses wanting to develop these areas must obtain special permits through Section 404 of the United States Clean Water Act. In many cases, when permits are issued, developers are required to **mitigate**, or create new wetlands, to make up for those that are lost. Though wetland destruction is not occurring at the rate it once was, wetland losses are still greater than wetland gains through restoration or mitigation efforts.

Wetlands provide a transition between **terrestrial** and **aquatic** habitats. They are generally defined as areas often covered by shallow water that are capable of supporting plants with adaptations to grow under saturated conditions. Wetlands are very diverse habitats that include grassy marshes, forested swamps, and estuarine salt marshes. Wetlands serve many ecological functions. They protect against flooding by storing rainfall, thus regulating water levels of lakes and rivers. Wetlands also recharge groundwater supplies, protect against shoreline erosion, and improve water quality. Wetland plants share a unique adaptation, as well. **They can filter pollutants such as nitrates and phosphates from water, and, thereby "cleanse" the water of these and other pollutants**. Wetlands are very important habitats for wildlife. They provide important habitat for about one-third of the plant and animal species on the federal endangered species list. They also serve as nesting, migration, and wintering areas for more than half of North America's migrating bird species. Furthermore, many mammals and millions of fish, amphibians, and reptiles are dependent on wetlands for their survival. Finally, wetlands can offer numerous recreational and educational activities.

Procedure 1

Map Analysis of Wetland Loss in the United States

Examine the following maps of the continental United States, and the use the information in them to answer the following questions.

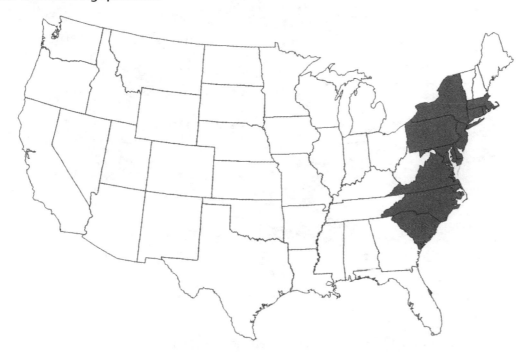

Figure 1: States with notable wetland losses (1600s to 1800).

Figure 2: States with notable wetland losses (1800 to 1860).

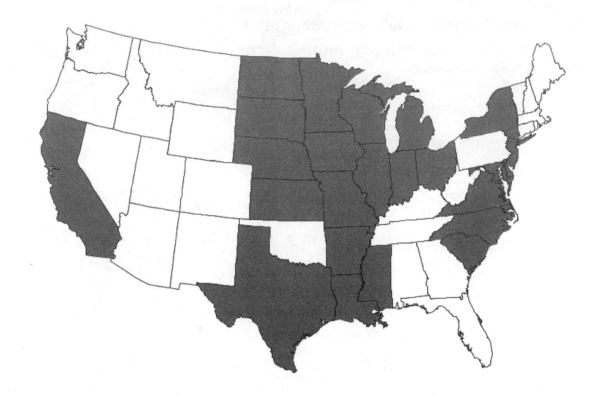

Figure 3: States with notable wetland losses (1860 to 1900).

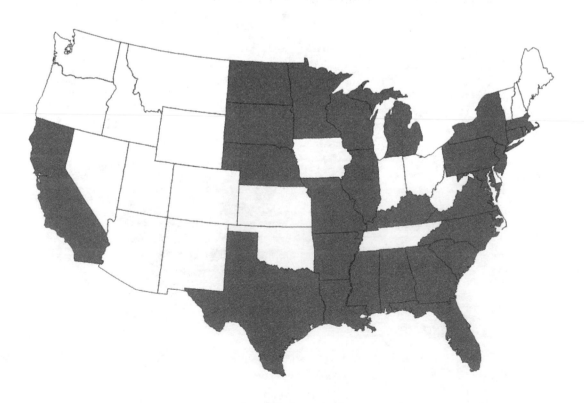

Figure 4: States with notable wetland losses (1900 to 1950).

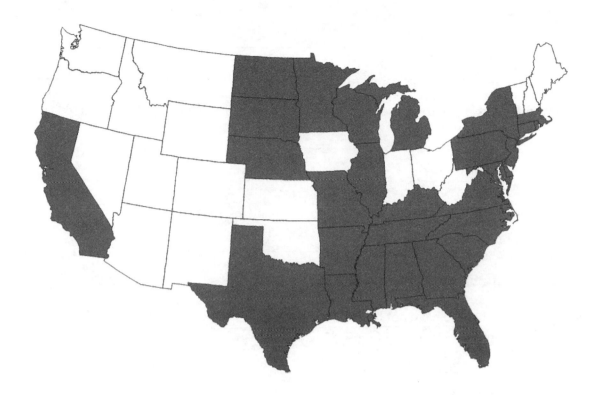

Figure 5: States with notable wetland losses (1950 to 1980).

Figure 6: Percentage of wetland acreage lost between (1780 and 1980).

1. In **Figure 1**, why do you think notable wetland losses occurred only in eastern states?

_____

_____

2. In **Figure 2**, why do you think most wetland losses occurred in the southeastern United States?

_____

_____

3. Which time periods appeared to have the most wetland losses? Why?

_____

_____

4. Which states appear to have not had many wetland losses throughout the last few hundred years? What may be some reasons for this?

_____

_____

5. Which three states have had the greatest percentage of wetland acreage lost? What may be some reasons for such extensive wetland losses in these three states?

North Carolina, southeastern, other southeast states

California, Illinois, Missouri

6. Which state had the lowest percentage of wetland acreage lost? Why?

southeast states, drying another

Alaska Hawaii, not a lot of wetlands

7. Examine the state you live in for each map. What is the percentage of wetland that has been lost in your state? During which time period did most of these losses occur?

1900 - 1980, -46

_____

8. In your opinion, what may be some ways you can help protect wetlands where you live?

Reduce runoff

_____

Water Quality and Water Conservation

Water is a finite resource that is often taken for granted. The fact that drinking water is a limited resource may come as a surprise to most people, especially when there appears to be so much water around us. Unfortunately for humans, 97% of the Earth's water is contained in the oceans as salt water. Of the remaining 3% of water on Earth that is fresh, 2.3% is trapped within glaciers and polar ice caps. This means that only 0.7% of all the Earth's water is fresh and usable for human needs. This is particularly grim when put in perspective of the needs of the global population. We are approaching a population of 6 billion people on our planet, and with so little fresh water to go around, the need for water conservation becomes obvious.

What might be some ways you can help conserve fresh water?

_____

_____

_____

Of the 0.7% of usable freshwater, 97% is located underground as **groundwater**. The remaining 3% is in lakes, rivers, streams, and wetlands. This water is continuously recycled through the Earth's **water cycle**. Water from oceans, lakes, streams, and even living organisms evaporates into the air. In the atmosphere, this water vapor condenses on fine dust particles and forms clouds. Clouds continue to form until, eventually, precipitation falls in the form of rain, snow, or sleet. This precipitation seeps back into the ground and becomes groundwater, or runs off into streams and rivers until the water cycle repeats itself.

Though the water cycle helps to purify our water, the only pure water is distilled water. Water contamination can come from two sources: point and non-point. **Point sources** refer to specific sites where contamination occurs, whereas **non-point sources** come from larger areas. For example, runoff containing fertilizers from farm fields may be considered a non-point source of contamination. Contaminants to water supplies are removed in water-treatment facilities. These facilities cleanse water of various organic and inorganic chemical substances in municipal water supplies.

What do you think would happen if you were to drink water that has not been cleansed in a water-treatment facility?

_____

_____

_____

Guidelines for water quality are determined by the **Environmental Protection Agency (EPA)**. The following table indicates several chemicals that may be found in water, their origins, and their allowable limits for consumption.

Table 1: EPA Primary Drinking Water Standards for Safe and Healthy Water Quality.

Chemical Substance	Origin	Allowable Limits
Ammonia	Bacterial decomposition of organic wastes and excretions of aquatic animals	Less than 1.0 ppm
Chlorine	Added by water treatment facilities to kill microorganisms in the water	Less than 0.5 ppm
Iron	Naturally occurring from igneous and sandstone rocks, corrosion of plumbing materials	Less than 0.2 ppm
Nitrate	Farm fertilizer, industrial waste, sewage, biological waste, naturally-forming mineral deposits	Less than 4.0 ppm

Some other characteristics of water include alkalinity, hardness, and pH. These factors are important not only for safe drinking water, but also for the well-being of aquatic ecosystems. Standards for these factors are listed in the following table.

Table 2: EPA Secondary Drinking Water Standards for Safe and Healthy Water Quality.

Chemical Substance	Description	Ideal Range
Alkalinity	Buffering capacity; prevents drastic pH fluctuations	20 to 200 ppm
Hardness	Levels of dissolved minerals, particularly calcium and magnesium	5 to 50 ppm fresh ~6625 sea water
pH	Hydrogen ion concentration; Measure of a solution's acidity	6.5 to 8.5

Procedure 2

Water Quality Testing

In this procedure, you will test various water samples using water-testing kits provided in lab. You will test for the chemical substances and water characteristics described in **Tables 1 and 2**. The water samples will come from different sources, including regular tap water, wetland water, canal water, and ocean water. Each lab group will be assigned one of these sources to test. Follow the directions provided in the water-testing kits to conduct each of your water tests. Answer the following questions, and document the class data in the table below.

What is a good control for this experiment? ___DL water___

Table 3: Lab Tests of Water Quality Parameters.

	Distilled Water	~~Tap~~ Water *without*	Wetland Water *with*	Canal Water	Ocean Water
Ammonia	0	0	1	6	7
Chlorine	0	0	0	0	0
Iron	.02	.02	0	.02	0
Nitrate	0	0	0	0	0
Phosphate					
Alkalinity	0	120	180	80	80
Hardness	0	120	120	180	1000
pH	0	7.5	8	7	7

1. Which water samples had higher concentrations of the chemical substances? Which water samples had lower concentrations of these substances?

   ___Ocean wt wetland, distilled___

2. Why do you think you got the results that you did?

   ___these areas are exposed to___
   ___runff___

3. What may be some limitations of the water tests you just performed?

_____Unted_____ saple_____

_____

4. Assess the tap water sample according to the information provided in **Tables 1 and 2**. Is this healthy drinking water? Explain.

_____yes, It lonly good to drink_____

_____

_____

Next, your instructor will demonstrate nitrate and phosphate tests on two samples of wetland water. Both samples will have come from the same wetland. However, one will have wetland vegetation in it, and the other will not.

5. Which water sample do you think will have higher concentrations of nitrate and phosphate?

_____Wetlad_____

_____

_____

Table 4: Lab Tests of Wetland Nitrates and Phosphates.

	Wetland Water	Wetland Water with Vegetation
Nitrate	0	0
Phosphate		

6. Are these the results you would have expected? Why or why not?

_____No, they are the sae_____

_____

_____

Procedure 3

Analysis of a Natural Waterway

Figure 7 depicts a stream as it passes by various natural and man-made areas. Examine this diagram carefully. Using the information in this chapter as a guide, generally explain what happens to the water quality of the stream as it passes by each station.

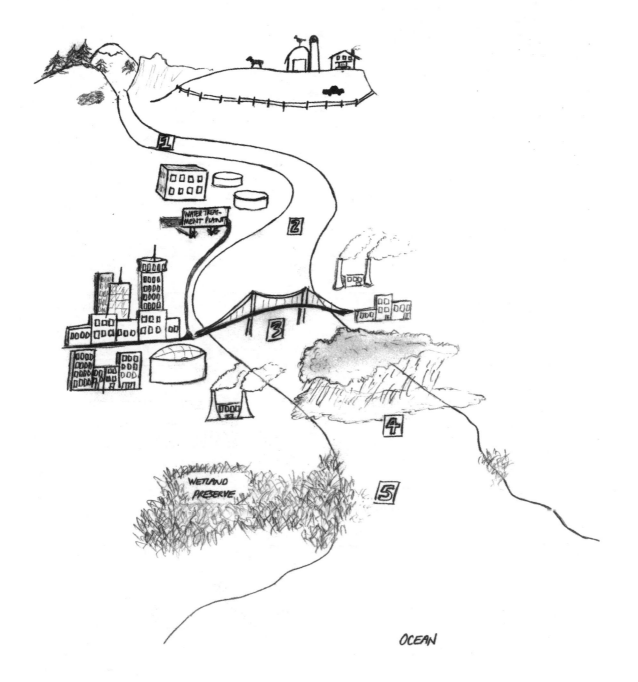

Figure 7: Stream analysis.

Station #1

water starb fresh

Station #2

people contaminate water
at first environment bad

Station #3

people start to see effects on
water

Station #4

bad water is cycled through
environment

Station #5

wetlands destroyed

What observations can you make about human influences on water quality?

if we print it bad, we
destroy environment

Critical Species

When a species becomes extinct, it is gone forever. **Extinction**, or the disappearance of a species from existence, occurs in all ecosystems. Species may become extinct though natural, evolutionary processes or though environmental pressures placed on them by outside forces, such as urbanization and pollution. In order to prevent extinction, federal, state and local governments have enacted legislation that establishes legal protection for species classified as **Endangered**, **Threatened**, or **Special Concern**. The most well-known piece of legislation is the **Endangered**

Species Act, which has afforded protection for species such as the California Condor, the Florida Panther, and the Manatee on a nation-wide basis. We will examine these classifications in order to understand their significance and the issues related to the protections afforded the listed species. Critical species can be listed either federally or according to individual state legislations.

Endangered species include any animal or plant species in danger of becoming extinct throughout its range. Threatened species include any animal or plant species that is not in immediate danger of extinction; however, these species face other environmental pressures that threaten their existence. A species is usually considered threatened before it is placed on the endangered species list. Programs to rehabilitate populations of threatened species are implemented when this determination is made. Captive breeding programs are examples of such rehabilitation efforts.

Special concern species include any species that has seen a major decline in population within its range. Once a species is listed, people cannot lawfully harass, shoot, hunt, or harm any individual of that species. This is the least amount of protection afforded to a species, as compared to a designation of endangered, which is the most protection afforded.

Efforts to protect endangered, threatened, or special concern species help to maintain **biodiversity**. Simply put, biodiversity is the compilation of all living species on Earth. Since 1600, more than 1200 species have disappeared, and some 32,000 species are in danger of extinction worldwide. When a species becomes extinct, part of this biodiversity is lost forever. This can have devastating consequences for nature and for people.

How may a loss of diversity affect nature?

Different crops will be affected CS
by animals as they go extinct

How might this affect humans?

we will become unhealthier

Critical species conservation or preservation of biodiversity is often a controversial issue. There can be many socioeconomic or cultural factors that may be negatively affected by a decision to protect an individual species. For example when the spotted owl of the Pacific Northwest was listed as a federally endangered species, many people in the logging profession were angered because this meant reductions in logging areas and, therefore, financial losses.

In the following procedure, you will learn to understand various points of view as they pertain to critical species conservation.

Procedure 4

Understanding Different Viewpoints

In this procedure, you will read the following case study on the threatened Florida Scrub Jay. After reading the case study, you will divide into groups of five. Within your group, each of you will be assigned a position to "act out" in a role-playing scenario, in which you will debate whether to set aside valuable land as a preserve for this species, or allow it to be developed. You will debate the point of view described in the position you are assigned. Only read your position, and **DO NOT** read the positions you were not assigned. Carefully talk through the issues. When you are finished, your group will have to come to a decision, and you will present this decision to the rest of your class.

Case Study: The Florida Scrub Jay

The Florida Scrub Jay is a threatened species with a limited range in central Florida. The Florida Scrub Jay is a subspecies of an otherwise prevalent and widespread bird species. However, long ago, when most of the Florida peninsula was covered in a shallow sea, the Florida Scrub Jay was confined to a small area of upland that remained above sea level. As time went on, the Florida Scrub Jay evolved distinct characteristics that separated it from its ancestors on the mainland. This species adapted to a localized area comprised of sand scrub habitat. Because it only occurs in this area, it is an **endemic** species to central Florida.

Florida Scrub jays are social birds that display significantly more parental care toward their young than other jay species. Young birds remain a member of the nest for years, and help their parents protect their siblings from predators and other threats. For this reason, Florida Scrub Jays are very loud, vocal birds.

Today, the Florida Scrub Jay may be in danger of losing its home. The scrub habitat this bird resides in is, itself, a rare habitat that is home to several other endemic species. Unfortunately, this habitat is prime upland in central Florida. Uplands are much easier to develop than wetlands, because developers are not restricted by wetland regulations. Florida has the most wetland area of any of the continental states. Therefore, with comparatively less upland area to support a continuously growing population, upland areas like this may have better uses as residential communities or citrus orchards.

The scrub ecosystem was untouched by citrus growers until it was discovered that this area is one of the best sites for growing oranges in the world. Unfortunately, the Scrub Jays depend on the slow-growing oak trees and palmetto plants that grow in these ecosystems. The Jays would not be able to sustain themselves if the native vegetation was replaced with orange trees. Still, Florida oranges are extremely popular, and the revenue they generate pays taxes for the state of Florida and supports thousands of citrus employees.

Florida Scrub Jays are not found anywhere else on earth. Once they are gone, they will be gone from the planet forever. Still, some people suggest that the Scrub Jay is just a unique strain of an otherwise common group of birds.

Should the sand scrub areas of central Florida be set aside for preservation of the Florida Scrub Jay, or should these areas be developed to support financial growth in the state?

Citizen #1 You are a developer in central Florida. Your specialty is designing and constructing retirement communities. You are particularly interested in developing the scrub area in central Florida because you feel this would be a popular area for retired senior citizens that may not want to live within the "hustle and bustle" of Florida's coasts. You know that more and more retirees are moving to Florida every day, and that this growing market could support many construction jobs. As far as you are concerned, the Florida Scrub Jay is an annoyance that may not allow you to carry out your plans.

Citizen #2 You are an ornithologist (a scientist that studies bird ecology) with Florida's chapter of the National Audubon Society. You have been fighting development pressures for years to save the sand scrub habitat and the endemic species that occur within it. You are fascinated by the uniqueness of this area. Even specialized cactus species can grow there! You know that very little scrub area remains, and you think the loss of this ecosystem may be a global tragedy. You are a firm believer in the right of every species on the planet to persist without being removed for financial gains.

Citizen #3 You are a citrus grower in central Florida. Your entire family has been involved in the citrus industry, and it is your family's sole source of income. Because of your family's long history in the business, you know what environmental conditions are most favorable for citrus growth. Nowhere else have you seen citrus trees produce better fruit than in the sandscrub habitats. You do not understand what the big deal is with the Florida Scrub Jay. It is just a noisy bird, like all other noisy birds. It is not as if you are going to clear-cut the entire area. You are going to be planting hundreds of trees, and birds love to nest in trees.

Citizen #4 You are a retiree living in central Florida. You have lived here for several years, and you enjoy going for walks and watching the Scrub Jays and gopher tortoises that live in the sand scrub area near your community. You are inspired by the strong sense of family these birds seem to exhibit. You enjoy nature, and you get your daily exercise by walking on trails in the sand scrub to watch your favorite birds. However, sometimes you miss your friends, and you wish there would be more retirement communities so they could move closer to you.

Citizen #5 You are a municipal planner in central Florida. It is your job to decide where developments can and cannot be built. You also authorize permits for different land uses, including citrus harvesting. You know the sand scrub area is unique and that it is habitat to critical species. You have been asked to revise the code that regulates what land use practices will be allowable on the sand scrub habitat. It is important that you understand the various viewpoints of the public. You are holding a town meeting to hear everyone's opinion before you make your final decision.

1. What did your group decide? Why did your group decide this?

_____

_____

_____

2. Was this decision easy or difficult to make? Why?

_____

_____

_____

3. What have you learned about critical species conservation?

_____

_____

_____

Literature Cited:

EPA. *Primary and Secondary Drinking Water Standards for Safe and Healthy Water Quality.*

On Common Ground, 1996. *Environmental Stewardship Pamphlet on Endangered Species.*

United States Geological Survey, 1997. *Water Supply Paper 2425.*

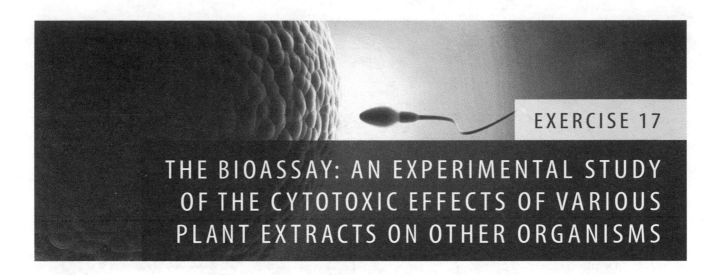

THE BIOASSAY: AN EXPERIMENTAL STUDY OF THE CYTOTOXIC EFFECTS OF VARIOUS PLANT EXTRACTS ON OTHER ORGANISMS

Objectives

The objectives of this exercise are to design and carry out experiments (bioassays) that test the cytotoxic effects of various plant extracts in three test organisms, *Artemia* (brine shrimp), Wisconsin Fast Plant (*Brassica rapa*) seeds, and *Bacillus cereus*, a type of bacteria. We will be performing bioassays on animal, plant and bacterial cells. We will also discuss the ecological role of several plant toxins and their potential effects on herbivores, competitors, and pathogens.

INTRODUCTION

Have you ever wondered why so many plants produce chemicals that are harmful to people or other animals? Some may cause you to develop a rash or other contact dermatitis, and some can be poisonous, or even deadly, if eaten. If you think about it, plants occupy the **producer** trophic level.

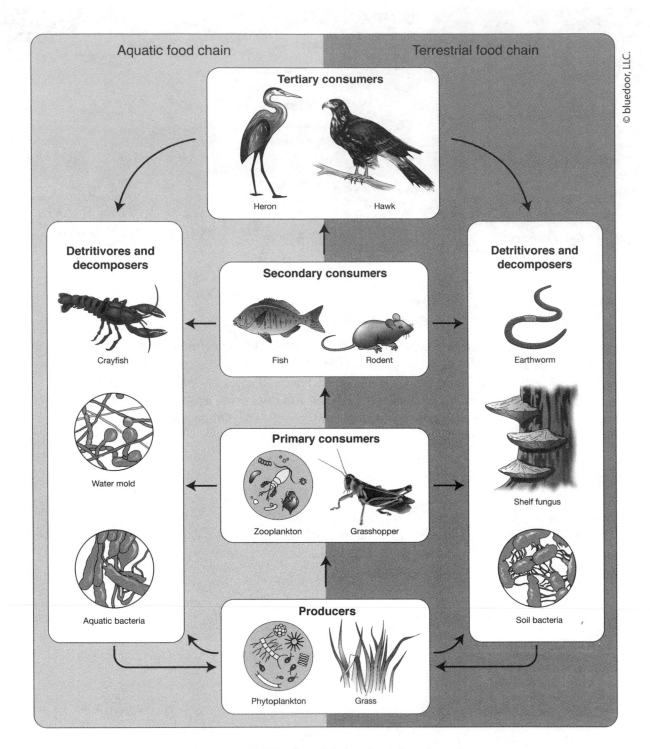

Figure 1: DIAGRAM of trophic levels and explanation.

They use solar energy to build organic compounds from carbon dioxide and water in the process known as photosynthesis. They also incorporate mineral nutrients they absorb from their roots in the soil into their own tissues. Plants compete with one another for these resources, and occupy the base of most food webs. Animals and other herbivore consumers eat plants in order to acquire the nutrients and energy stored within.

Since plants can't physically move to avoid predators, they often have thorns or tough tissues to physically defend themselves, as well as secondary compounds they use for chemical defense. They are called **secondary compounds** because they do not fall into the major chemical groups of carbohydrates, lipids, proteins or nucleic acids and are produced from biochemical pathways that are offshoots of basic metabolism. They occur sporadically in some species and not in others, and have no known role in the metabolism of these plants. Originally, these compounds were thought to be by-products of metabolism or "waste products", but because of their relatively high concentrations, further study was warranted. Secondary compounds are also very costly for the plants to produce, using energy that might compromise the growth and/or reproduction of the plant, which also suggests that these compounds are very important. Consider compounds like caffeine, nicotine, and strychnine that have all evolved in plants for defense against animal consumers, plant competitors, and pathogenic microbes that cause disease. An example of another one of these compounds is tannins. The tannins in the leaves of oaks and many other plants combine with the proteins in the leaves and digestive enzymes in an insect's gut to inhibit the digestion of protein of the insect and considerably slow or retard its growth. Tannins are also deterrents to herbivores because of their astringent, bitter taste and ability to precipitate or shrink proteins, which causes the dry mouth and puckering upon ingestion.

Evolutionary modifications of the physiological or biochemical systems in herbivores can sometimes counter the toxic effects of plants. Some herbivore species have been able to coevolve detoxification mechanisms of their own, thereby providing their own defense to plants (and their secondary compounds) that are toxic to most other species. An example familiar to most of us is the Monarch butterfly. The adult female lays her eggs on the milkweed (*Asclepias*) plants, where the eggs hatch into the larval form known as a caterpillar. The larvae eat the milkweed leaves that contain potent heart poisons that are toxic to almost all other herbivores, and are able to do so because they have evolved metabolic pathways to detoxify the milkweed poison. They also store this poison in their own tissues, which serves to protect them from their own predators.

Other chemicals that plants product act by different mechanisms. Some alter the growth or development of insects by interfering with hormone production. Others act as repellants that prevent feeding, and even other plant compounds have antibiotic properties that inhibit bacterial growth and infection.

In this exercise, we will examine the harmful effects of some of the plant compounds we've chosen on animals, plants and bacterial cells. We will focus particularly on those bioactive compounds that are cytotoxic (poisonous) to specific cell types. A **bioactive compound** is a compound that will show a specific biological effect on the survival, growth, or reproduction of another living organism; thus, a **bioassay** is an experimental screening for a potentially bioactive substance in a test population of living organisms in a controlled environment. Bioassays measure the quantity of a substance that produces a defined effective dose, and they are used for a number of purposes. Scientists use bioassays to screen plants for potentially useful naturally occurring drugs. Some of these drugs may be cytotoxic agents, like those used in chemotherapy for cancer cells. Many of the side effects associated with chemotherapy are due to the compound's cytotoxic effect on the other body cells, as well as the cancer cells. Scientists study the biochemical pathways affected by cytotoxins, understanding that cells that do not use these specific pathways are not affected by that compound or chemotherapeutic agent.

Although it is unlikely that you will find either unknown cancer-fighting drugs or undiscovered natural herbicides in this lab, you may very well find plants that contain cytotoxic agents. Remember that the reason those chemicals exist in nature is because of the coevolution between plants and their environments, including herbivores, competitors, or pathogens. There may be potential practical uses that evolve from the understanding that we gain from simple bioassays. In this lab we will first use two test organisms and your choice of a number of plants purchased for this investigation. The first test organism, *Artemia,* or brine shrimp, are tiny crustaceans that thrive in salty environments. They are filter-feeders that sweep algae and other food particles into their mouths, and are, thus, **primary consumers** in an aquatic ecosystem. (see **Figure 1**) This bioassay will look for cytotoxic effects on certain cells in *Artemia* as an indicator of the presence of cytotoxic compounds in a plant extract.

The next test organism is a plant seed, *Brassica rapa,* one of the Wisconsin Fast Plants from Carolina Biological Supply. These Fast Plants are small, rapidly growing seeds of plants in cabbage family, and potential herbicidal (plant-killing) compounds or even stimulants for plant growth can be identified by testing the effects of the plant extract on seed germination and plant growth over 24 hours. Lastly, we will investigate the cytotoxic effect of garlic on bacteria.

EXPERIMENTAL DESIGN

Working in groups of four, you will investigate the effects of plant secondary compounds on cell survival in Artemia and seed germination and growth in Fast Plants. Plants (or plant materials) available for testing will include (but not be limited to) the following: fresh rosemary, tarragon, oregano, or other fresh herbs, horseradish root, lemongrass stems and leaves, fresh ginger root, dandelion leaves, dried cloves, dried mustard seeds, black peppercorns, and ground coffee beans.

Your group will develop a hypothesis that you will test looking at your plant extract's effect on the following:

(1) Artemia cell survival.

(2) Fast Plant seed germination and growth.

There is no single correct hypothesis for either experiment. Remember that a hypothesis is usually based on an observation. Our group will test the following hypotheses:

(1)

(2)

Design two experiments using the materials in the lab to test your hypotheses. What is your experimental design?

(1)

(2)

What is your control for the first experiment?

For the second?

In each case, state your predictions.

What are the possible general outcomes of experiment (1)?

For experiment (2)?

You may divide up the work among group members and share data. Make sure everyone in your group has a clearly defined set of tasks, but share not only your results, but predictions and conclusions.

BIOASSAY PROCEDURES

A. Preparation of plant extract

1. If using leaf tissue, use a scalpel to avoid any large veins. If using root tissue, remove soil by washing. Grind the tissue in the mortar and pestle for 5-10 minutes (no less) to rupture the plant cells and spill their contents into the bioassay liquid.

2. Measure 2 0.1 g samples of the plant paste onto 2 pieces of weighing paper or weighing boats. Place one sample in a beaker containing 10 ml brine (salt solution) for the *Artermia* experiment. Place the other sample in another beaker containing 10 ml dH20 for the plant experiment. Stir to create uniform suspensions. The extract has a final concentration of 10 mg/ml.

B. Artemia Bioassay

1. Label 2 microscope slides, one "negative control", and one "positive control." Each group will receive a small beaker of *Artemia* in brine. Place a brine shrimp on each slide, and blot small drop of excess brine with paper towel. The brine shrimp will be surrounded in a small brine droplet only. Swirl the trypan blue stain to evenly mix, and pipet one drop on the brine shrimp on each slide. The brine shrimp shouldn't be swimming, but covered by the liquid. Blot excess stain, if necessary.

2. Next, place the negative control slide on the stage of the microscope under low power. Observe the structure, and notice how the tail resides somewhat behind the main body (see **Figure 2**).

3. Using a sharp micro-scalpel, cut approximately ½ of the tail away. Place a coverslip on top of the severed tail sections, and observe both cut ends of the tail. Notice the small, round cells emerging from each portion of the tail cavity. These are **amoebocytes,** and are the subject cells of our bioassay because they respond similarly to human cells to cytotoxic agents. Healthy and living cells appear colorless and ghostlike, and do not pick up trypan blue stain. Dead or damaged cells appear blue, as they take up the stain.

4. In a field of view with minimal movement, count the number of colorless cells and the number of blue cells out of a total of 25 cells total. Calculate the percentage of dead cells. This is the "Background" rate for dead cells. Record this data in **Table 1**.

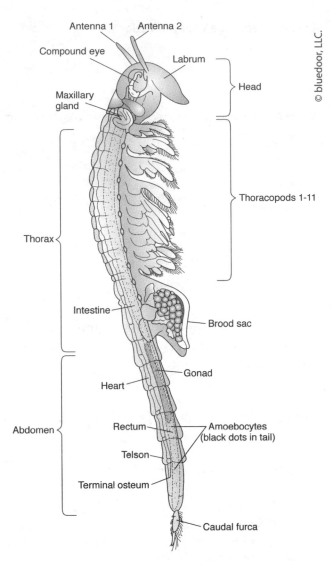

© bluedoor, LLC.

Figure 2: *Artemia.*

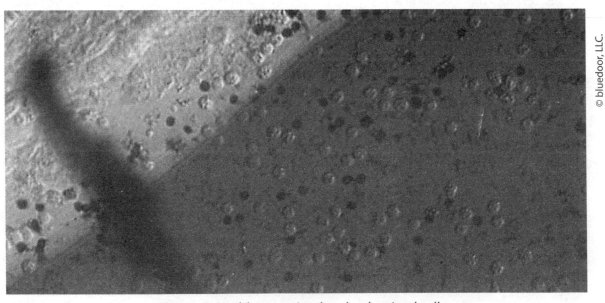

© bluedoor, LLC.

Figure 3: Healthy unstained vs dead stained cells.

5. Now, do the same for the positive control, but after cutting the section of tail away, add a drop of acetic acid (commercial vinegar strength) before topping with a coverslip. Acetic acid is a potent cytotoxin. After 1-2 minutes, under low power, count the number of colorless and blue cells out of a total of 25, as above. Calculate the percentage of dead cells and record. This number illustrates the effects of a strong cytotoxin on Artemia amoebocytes. If you see no dead (stained) cells, wait up to 30 minutes to repeat the count, so that the cytotoxic effect is visible.

6. Test your plant extract(s) in a similar fashion, depending upon your experimental design, but using the same format as the positive control, adding 1-2 drops of plant extract instead of the acetic acid to your brine shrimp/stain mixture. Add a coverslip, and wait the same number of minutes that it took for the positive control to be positive. Record your data in the table below.

Table 1: Effect of Plant Extracts on *Artemia*.

TREATMENT	CONTENTS	#UNSTAINED (LIVE) CELLS	# STAINED (DEAD) CELLS	% DEAD CELLS
Negative control	Brine + trypan blue			0
Positive control	Brine + trypan blue + acetic acid			50
Plant extract 1	Brine + trypan blue + plant extract 1			25
Plant extract 2	Brine + trypan blue + plant extract 2			
Plant extract 3	Brine + trypan blue + plant extract 3			

C. Fast Plant Bioassay

1. Obtain 4 microcentrifuge tubes and label with the following: 10, 1, 0.1, and Control. Place 10 drops of plant extract into tube labeled 10. This tube contains 10 mg/ml of the plant extract. You will now make serial dilutions of that solution, resulting in concentrations of 1 mg/ml and 0.1 mg/ml.

2. To the tubes labeled 1 and 0.1, add 9 drops of dH20. Place in decending order in microfuge rack. See **Figure 4.**

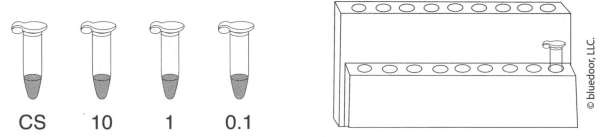

Figure 4: Microcentrifuge tubes and microfuge holder.

© bluedoor, LLC.

3. Pipet liquid from tube 10, and add 1 drop to tube 1. Return unused liquid to tube 10. Place cap on tube 1, invert, and mix thoroughly. The concentration of tube 1 (after 1:10 dilution) is 1 mg/ml.

4. From tube 1, pipet liquid and add 1 drop to tube labeled 0.1. Return unused liquid in pipet to tube 1. Cap and mix tube 0.1 thoroughly. This tube now contains a 1% solution of the original tube 10 or a 0.1 mg.ml concentration.

5. Pipet 10 drops of dH20 to the tube labeled "control."

6. Insert a paper towel wick into each microcentrifuge tube. Place two RCBr Fast Plant seeds near the top of each wick, and close the caps on each tube, making sure that the wick does not stick out of the cap.

7. Rubber band your 4 tubes together so they stand upright and can be transported home safely. After 24-30 hours, examine the tubes from your bioassay to see how many and which seeds germinated. Measure in mm the roots and shoots of each seed, and record in **Table 2**. If your experimental design called for a second plant extract, record those results in **Table 3**.

Table 2: Effect of Plant Extract_____ on Germination of Fast Plant Seeds.

TUBE	Germ Y/N Seed 1	Germ Y/N Seed 2	Root mm Seed 1	Root mm Seed 2	Shoot mm Seed 1	Shoot mm Seed 2
Control dH20						
10 mg/ml						
1 mg/ml						
.01 mg/ml						

D. Results/Analysis

Do your results indicate any cytotoxicity of the plant extract(s) that you used? _____

_____

_____

What is your conclusion regarding the effect of your plant extract(s) on plant and/or animal cells specifically? _____

_____

_____

How do these conclusions support or refute your hypotheses? _____

_____

_____

Why have secondary compounds evolved in plants? _____

_____

_____

Why would a chemical that is cytotoxic to Artemia not necessarily have a similar effect on plant cells?

_____

_____

How would a pharmaceutical company use a bioassay to identify potential drug compounds from the sawgrass in the Everglades and their affect on potential pathogens? **Note:** these experiments don't involve Artemia or Fast Plants.

_____

_____

_____

_____

_____

_____

If you found that seed germination took place at 1 mg/ml, but none took place at .1 mg/ml, what would your next experiment be to determine the actual effective concentration? _____

_____

_____

_____

How might you alter the *Artemia* experiment to provide more information? _____

_____

_____

_____

Prep Notes:

Working Trypan Blue stain is made using 5 ml 0.4% stock solution (Sigma T 8154-100ml) diluted with 20 ml brine solution.

Brine solution is made using Instant Ocean 255 gm added to 3200 ml d H_2O.

E. Bacterial Cell Bioassay

Bacillus cereus is a gram-positive, spore forming, rod-shaped bacteria from the same family as the anthrax-producing *Bacillus anthracis*. Although it is less harmful, and can even act beneficially as a probiotic, *Bacillus cereus* can still cause some "cereus" discomfort! It is often responsible for the nausea, vomiting, cramping and diarrhea associated with food poisoning. Even cooking food cannot always eliminate the risk of *Bacillus cereus* food poisining because its spores are heat resistant: they can survive brief exposure to cooking and boiling temperatures. The heat stable toxin produced by *Bacillus cereus* can cause skin and eye infections, which can eventually lead to pneumonia and meningitis, among other diseases.

The most common treatment for a *Bacillus cereus* infection is oral rehydration; however, a more serious infection requires antibiotics. Unfortunately, misuse of antibiotics is resulting in a growing number of pathogens developing antibiotic resistant properties. As pathogens develop the ability to evade antibiotics, we are losing the ability to treat common infections. This antibiotic resistance may eventually cause a world-wide plague that we have no way to treat. For this reason, it is essential that researchers develop alternatives to antibiotics and that doctors have treatments available (other than overprescribed antibiotics) for bacterial infections. One possible solution is more common than you might expect; in fact, you likely have it in your kitchen at this very moment!

We've all heard that garlic can protect against vampires, but it turns out that garlic can protect us against more realistic dangers, as well. One of the earliest documented plants to be used as a treatment for and prevention of disease, garlic has been used as a remedy for everything from graying hair in India to infections and epilepsy in Ancient Greece. It is believed that Garlic was used to improve strength and endurance in slaves in Ancient Egypt, Olympic athletes in Ancient Greece and soldiers and sailors in Ancient Rome. Even Hippocrates, considered the father of modern medicine, recognized the medicinal benefits of garlic; he used it to treat infections, epilepsy, toothaches, wounds, chest pains and intestinal disorders. With such a long and prolific history as a tonic and a cure-all treatment, it is no wonder that garlic contains a substance that confers antioxidant, antibacterial, antifungal, antiviral, and antiprotozoal properties. This substance is called **allicin**.

Allicin, the componenet responsible for garlic's strong smell, is created from alliin (contained in garlic) by the enzyme alliinase when garlic is cut or crushed. Alllicin is an example of a **bioactive compound**; it serves to protect garlic from pests. Allicin has also been shown to be more effective than penicillin in treating a number of diseases, including typhus, strep, staph, cholera, dysentery and enteritis. Allicin exerts these medical benefits by blocking cysteine proteinase, an infection-related enzyme that enables bacteria to invade and damage tissue, and alcohol dehydrogenase, an enzyme that supports survival of infectious organisms.

Garlic's history of health-related uses and its conversion to allicin when injured strongly implicate garlic as a valuable medicinal plant. Its ability to act as a natural antibiotic is becoming increasingly important as we encounter a growing number of drug-resistant bacteria. In this exercise, we will put garlic's antibiotic capability to the test by conducting a bacterial cell **bioassay**.

Bacterial Cell Bioassay Procedures

1. Prepare a **bacterial lawn** on a nutrient agar plate for microbiological antibacterial-resistant testing by dipping a sterile loop into the bacterial culture and following the plate-streaking directions below.

Streak a vertical line of bacteria.

Spread the streak left to right, moving from the top to the bottom. (in black)

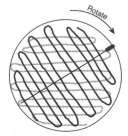

Rotate the plate 60 degrees clockwise and again spread the bacteria going left to right, top to bottom. (in gray)

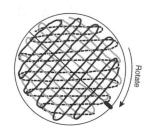

Rotate the plate 60 degrees clockwise and again spread the bacteria going left to right, top to bottom. (in black dotted)

2. Prepare garlic-soaked discs.

   a. Peel garlic cloves and wash them in running water.

   b. Crush the cloves, add distilled water and mix.

   c. Add paper discs to the garlic paste solution.

3. Prepare control by placing paper discs into a separate beaker of distilled water.

4. Divide nutrient agar plate into two sections by drawing a line through the middle on the bottom of the plate. Label one side 'Distilled Water' and label the other side 'Garlic'. Place one disc (from the corresponding solution) onto each half. Be sure to place the disc on the side so that it is correctly labeled. Be sure to press the discs firmly into place so that they will not fall when the agar plate is turned upside down.

5. Place cover on the nutrient agar plate and incubate agar side down at 37° C for up to 48 h, then store at room temperature.

6. Dispose of the sterile loop used for streaking the bacteria into the biohazardous waste receptacle. Clean the lab bench using the provided disinfectant, and wash hands with soap and warm water. It is especially important to clean thoroughly after this lab in order to avoid contamination with *Bacillus cereus*.

7. (This step will be completed in the following week, after cultures have been incubated.) Measure the diameter of the **zone of inhibition**, the clear area around the disc, in order to determine how effective each solution was at killing *Bacillus cereus*.

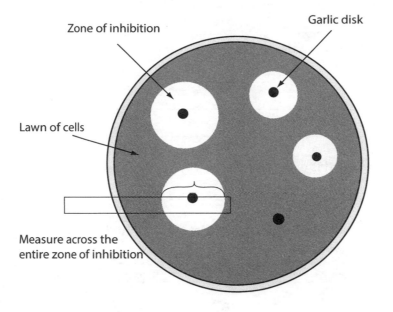

Zone of inhibition

Garlic disk

© bluedoor, LLC.

Lawn of cells

Measure across the
entire zone of inhibition

Results

Distilled water
Zone of Inhibition =
_____ cm

Garlic
Zone of Inhibition =
_____ cm

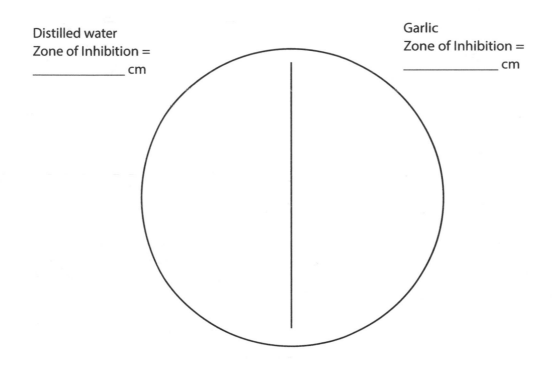

Questions:

1. What effect did garlic have on the *Bacillus cereus* culture?

_____

_____

_____

2. What was the control in this experiment?

_____

3. If bacteria did not grow on either side of the plate, what would be some possible conclusions? Try to think of at least two possibilities.

_____

_____

_____

4. Knowing that garlic is antibiotic and cytotoxic to *Bacillus cereus*, what would be a possible conclusion if the bacterial culture grew well on both sides of the plate (despite the garlic disc)?

_____

_____

_____

5. How could you test the antibacterial properties of different concentrations of garlic paste?

_____

_____

_____

6. Imagine garlic was not commonly consumed. Once recognizing its antibacterial properties, you might want to market it for medicinal purposes, but you would first want to make sure it wasn't toxic to normal human cells. Describe how you could modify this experiment in order to test garlic's cytotoxicity against human cells.

_____

_____

_____

_____

_____

_____

Vocabulary

allicin _____

bacterial lawn _____

bioactive compound _____

bioassay _____

cytotoxic _____

zone of inhibition _____

References

Chand, B. *Antibacterial effect of garlic* (Allium sativum) *and Ginger* (Zingiber officinale) *against* Staphylococcus aureus, Salmonella, Typhi, Escherichia coli *and* Bacillus cereus. J of Microbiology, Biotechnology and Food Sciences. 2013: 2(4) 2481 – 2491.

Fonseca, M.J and Tavares, F. *Natural Antibiotics: A hands-on activity on garlic's antibiotic properties.* The American Biology Teacher. 2011; 73: 342 – 346.

Rivlin R.S. *Historical perspective on the use of garlic.* J Nutr. 2001; 131: 951S–954S.

Working Trypan Blue stain is made using 5 ml 0.4% stock solution (Sigma T 8154-100ml) diluted with 20 ml brine solution.